From the CORNER to the CASTLE

ISBN- 13: 978-1732396609 (paperback)
ISBN- 10: 1732396604

Published by Pen 2 Pen Publishing
Est. 2012

Printed in the U.S.A.

This is an authorized biography of Larry Everett. Names, locales, places, events, and people contained herein are purely from the author's memory, and/or from public record. This story is not intended to defame, intimidate, or ridicule any persons, living or dead.

Email: contact@ larryeverettpublishing.com

From the CORNER to the CASTLE

By: Larry Everett

Acknowledgments

I wanna acknowledge God first. I'm quadruple blessed, and without him none of this would be possible. Shout out to my grandmother Bessie "May" Smalls. I love this woman more than life! Her many teachings and life lessons along with her constant prayers have brought me a long way. That's my heart. Shout out to Dee from Savoy Heights. I can't explain your loyalty and sweetness. It's unheard of. You dedicated your life to supporting ole' Longhead and for that I'm forever thankful. I got yo' back like a spinal cord. Just say it and it's done. Shout out to Lauryn. I'm trying to see the best way to explain the way I feel about her... breathtaking! My lil' 4 year-old daughter. Even when I have more kids, there will always be something special about my firstborn. There is something that came over my whole body when I heard that little girl say Daddy. Shout out to my unborn seeds, I promise to love you and break my neck for you before you even make it to the land. My sis, Mek-Mek, Khapreshan, Kiera, Chug, Eliza, my stepmom Angie, and my pops, I love y'all. My Aunt Boogie, I love you too baby. You still looking 27 girl (LOL). That's about it, I guess. As you grow in life, the less people you have to love because you outgrow them.

FOREWORD

I'm so disappointed in y'all niggas. I'm at a loss for words. It's funny how you niggas think y'all talking like G's when you really sounding like bitches, sneak dissing, assassinating real niggas' character behind their back. Real niggas don't move like that, homie. That's why I'm the opposite of you fuck niggas. Twenty years in the game, militant minded, trained to fall asleep in the bullpen. I made a vow to remain solid. Even God won't forgive you! Don't believe me? Check the 9th Commandment: Thou Shalt Not Bear False Witness.

Loyalty is not just a word to me, it's my language, my culture, my way of life. I stand ten toes down for what I believe in. I apologize to all the real niggas. I been so caught up doing other shit I got going on. I should've been had this book to you...

PROLOGUE

"I'm gonna kill you, motherfucker! I'm gonna shoot you in your head. Don't beg now. Tell the ones before you I said, what's up. You ready to meet your maker?"

"Baby, baby, wake up!" Destiny screamed.

"I'm woke, Destiny! What's wrong?" Richard barked, agitated.

"Richard, baby, you were dreaming again." Destiny sighed. "You have nightmares every night, Richard. You're such a good guy, baby. Why do you have nightmares all the time? I'm starting to get worried for you. I'm in love with you, Richard. Is there anything you wanna tell me? I'm here for you, baby."

"Destiny baby, if I tell you my life story that means we are gonna be graveyard friends."

"Richard, what does that mean?" Destiny asked.

"Destiny, that means you gotta take everything I tell you to the graveyard—Mo taught me that."

"Baby, who is Mo? Baby are you still dreaming?" Destiny asked. "Richard, you're so sweet, you're the sweetest boyfriend I ever had. But it seems something is bothering you, like you've been through some complicated events in your life. Richard are you sleep while I'm talking?"

"No, Destiny," I assured her. "Just remember what I told you: once I tell you my past, that makes us graveyard friends."

"I know, Richard. Mo taught you that. I heard you, baby. I pinky promise... Now, who is Mo? Tell me Richard, we are graveyard friends now."

"Destiny I can't remember, where was I? I can hardly remember... Oh yeah, that's right! Destiny, I was left on my grandmother's porch on Clark Street with a baby bib, one bottle half-filled with spoiled milk from the heat, and two diapers. And the story went like this…

"May who is that baby crying at that front door..."

Wherever you go, you always leave a foot print. Well, here is mine.

Table of Contents

CHAPTER 1

Troubling Childhood

James Allen once said something in one of his books that I read that has stuck with me through the years. I mean, I knew the quote and could spit it out verbatim for an extra push, or to aid someone's perception of my intelligence, but knowing something is a far cry from understanding that same thing. It was like I didn't grasp the context, or clear meaning of what he meant until it was pushed in my face and my immediate survival depended on my next move. The quote said, '*Whatever your present environment may be, you will rise or fall by your thoughts, your vision, your ideal.*'

I've wished so many times that I would have understood the meaning of those words a long time ago. I'm almost positive that I would've ended up a completely different person than I am today. A lawyer or doctor maybe. Who knows, I might've become the next Bill Gates, or Tom Strayer. We all know that I didn't become any of these things. Because, if I had, you wouldn't be reading this book about what I did become. And that is the Alpha Male of my pack, a goon, goblin, soldier, and General all wrapped up in one body. Oh, don't get it twisted; I didn't become who I am overnight. I was built from the ground up. Through blood, sweat, tears, and years of focusing and concentrating on where I saw myself being in the future, I became the man that I am. See, I learned something early on in life that has kept me as a front runner in whatever campaign I was in at that moment. It was as simple as this: life isn't about finding yourself, it's about *creating* yourself over and over again, until you make the best *you* that you can possibly be. And the fact of the matter is, as long as you are happy with you, then to hell with the haters. Live life, love the baddest bitch, and laugh as much as you can. There are no do-overs in life. No rewind or pause button. This movie only has play and fast forward. So, I hope that each eye that reads this book understands that I, Larry "Longhead" Everett, lived this shit called life to the fullest and I have no regrets.

They say that time heals all wounds. Well, for me, I am sure that it'll take a whole bunch of time because I have more wounds than the normal impoverished guy from the proverbial ghetto. However, before we go any further, let's pause and get some things straight about me.

First, I am a problem. There's no doubt about it. I've been a problem for as long as I can remember. It's just that, these days, I am my own problem versus being a problem to and for other people. I remember being innocent – no, let me stop lying. I've never been innocent! I've always been hell on wheels. Hell, since birth I think. If I didn't know any better, I'd be willing to bet that I was that kid trying to sell breast milk to other babies while I was in the hospital. I've always been a hustler. My parents were hustlers. So, it's safe to say that it was already in my blood when I was brought into this world. People always say that, "*trouble don't last always.*" Well, I am still here, so I guess it's still lasting.

I have so many stories to tell, but nothing is better than starting at the beginning.

I was born to Tiny (Koo Koo) Everett, and Larry Longhead Small on June 20, 1984. Now, that was a monumental day, and I was a monumental kid, but they didn't want me. Why? I don't know. I guess the love of the streets is sometimes more powerful than the love of family. I guess it all worked out because if they wanted me, and raised me in their way, you probably wouldn't be reading this story.

I was actually raised by my grandmother, Bessie "May" Small. That, dear people, is my favorite girl. Besides my daughter – who we'll get to in due time – my grandmother is the love of my life. My sun rises and falls around that woman. Now my granddad, he's a whole different entity altogether, who unconsciously played a major role in who I eventually became. Why? Because he didn't want me either.

It may be difficult, but at least try to imagine being a five-year-old kid, sleeping on your grandparents' couch, being forced to endure painful conversations every day. I could recall it like it was this morning...

"May, when they coming to pick that boy up?" Granddad said in his husky voice, as he sat at the kitchen table watching my grandma sweating over a stove to fix him a plate. Her shoulders were slumped over in exasperation because she'd heard this same conversation a million times before. "Don't you hear me talking to you, woman? I said, when they coming to pick that boy up?"

I could hear them loud and clear. Their voices were like magnets pulling me closer to the kitchen where all the drama was going down.

I inched closer to the kitchen, each silent step sending a jolt through my small body. My granddad's voice carried malicious intent on every wave, as if he wanted to end my existence with his heavy tongue. As I reached the corner of the wall, I could see him sitting like the King of the castle, staring at my grandmother's back as she fixed his food.

"May!!" He yelled again. "You need to tell me something because my patience is wearing thin."

I could see my grandmother's whole body stiffen. I felt it before she turned around. I could see the fire in her eyes. Her beautiful face went from calm to a mask of pure defiance.

"Let's get one thing straight, Map," she said, looking him dead in the eyes without a hint of fear. "That boy has a name, and it's Larry. So, don't keep calling my baby out of his name. Second, we are family, and family takes care of one another through every situation. Family doesn't turn tail and run when they are needed. And last, he *is* home, Map. And this will always be his home for as long as God sees fit to breathe in my body!"

She slammed his dinner down in front of him so hard I almost pissed in my pants. It was like I was stuck in that one spot forever, afraid to move, speak, or even blink. Hell, if I could've stopped breathing, I probably would've. Time seemed to move slow before my granddad finally broke the silence.

"Well May," he started, and cleared his throat. "I don't feel like I have to deal with raising someone else's problem."

"You don't," my grandmother whispered, with her back turned to him again.

"What!" He roared. "What was that?"

Grandma turned around so fast I barely caught the spin. She put her hands on the table, elbows locked in place, and gave him her full attention. "I said, you don't," she repeated. "You don't have to deal with anyone's problem, because he is not a problem. He's our grandchild, and I'm not about to let no system raise my baby. If he has to abide by someone's rules, they might as well be mine."

"I understand all that," he said. "But I am the man of this house, so either he goes or I go."

"Well don't let the door hit cha' where the good Lord split cha," my grandmother replied, with a hand on her wide hip.

I ran to the couch and threw the covers over my face. My grandfather stormed past me without saying a word. All I heard was the door slam, and then silence. Well, not total silence, because I could hear myself. I could hear myself crying like I've done fifty times before this incident. For some reason, I couldn't wrap my tiny head around the *why?* I knew the *how*. How I came to be here was because my wack-ass parents chose their want over my needs. But why? Why was I the topic of each conversation? Why was my name being whispered among my family members, my aunts talking about how worthless my parents are, or my cousins teasing me constantly about how I was homeless and didn't even have a room of my own, with pictures and posters, or comic books like every other six-year-old on the planet.

Why? That was the million-dollar question running around in my head.

I was still crying and questioning my existence when my grandmother sat down beside me and slid the covers off my face. As I stared up at her, tears raced down my cheeks like rain on a window pane and my lips wouldn't stop quivering. She sat staring at me for a short while before she reached out and scooped me up in her arms. She laid me against her chest and kissed me on the forehead. My faucet of tears slowed to a mist as she took her hand and wiped the fallen tears from my shiny cheeks.

"Now hush up; big boys don't cry every time they are hurt."

I gave a slight hiccup before asking, "Why don't nobody love me?"

"I love you baby," she sang. "And as long as I love you, it don't matter who don't, because I got enough love for everybody. I just keep a little bit extra for you."

"You do?" I asked, already knowing the answer but needing to hear it again just to appease my little soul.

My grandmother sighed and pulled me in close. "Listen baby, let grandma tell you something I don't want you to ever forget," she said. "Everybody is going to hurt you, Larry. But you have to figure out who is worth the pain. I know if I leave this earth today you will be the one to survive, because you're tough. No matter what anybody says out of their mouth, I know that you are the toughest little boy in the world."

"Tougher than Super Man?" I asked.

"Even tougher than Super Man," she sang back. "But you know why?"

I shook my head because I really didn't know why. Maybe she was just saying all this to make me feel better.

"Because you are my little Larry. And *I* am tough, so you don't have much choice but to be tough too," she explained. "Now stop that crying and let's go get us something to eat."

That was just one episode out of a million that took place at my grandparents' house. It was always back and forth. It seemed like everybody had an opinion about where I should sleep, eat, or bathe. Everybody wanted what *they* wanted for me, when all I wanted was someone to love me like a child supposed to be loved. Like the kids I see daily with their parents. I didn't care where the love came from, or who gave it. I just wanted the love.

Looking back on it now, the crazy part about it is that I am who I am because they were who they were. If I could do it all over, I wouldn't change a damn thing. They threw me to the wolves and I didn't bend, break, nor fold. I did way better than that. I came back leading the pack. Watch this!!!

I was only a kid. I couldn't figure out what I did for everybody to hate me for no reason, and why no one loved me.

CHAPTER 2
Transition

Let me start this thing off with a little bit about the environment that made the man you know today. It was crazy, wild, humbling, and *turnt* up like most hoods. But my hood, at least to me, was the shit!

I've seen things that a normal 12-year-old boy wouldn't have been able to fathom. Life, for me, was a roller coaster ride from the word, *go.* I'm talking about from an infant to adulthood, from baby to boss. I am sure I've experienced it all, and if I didn't see it for myself, then I had an uncle, aunt or cousin who saw it and could tell the story like a Lionsgate movie.

I don't think there is another place like Haymount Hill, no other street like Clark Street, no 'Ville like Fayetteville.

Clark Street is at the bottom of Raeford Road, and if Fayetteville was a body, then Clark Street would be the heart. To me, this was the epicenter of everything that was happening in the City. Let's just say we had everything we needed – not always what we wanted, but always what we needed. When I was young I would've bet my life that the 'Ville bred gangsters like cattle. Everywhere you looked around it was going down, and if you couldn't hold your own in the jungle, then the predators were on that ass like flies on shit. I learned early on, the ones that survived in my hood were built for whatever, those that weren't scared to die and equally ready to kill whenever that day came. That didn't just apply to men either; the women in my hood put on for their city too. They could drink, smoke, curse, roll dice, shoot, and out hustle any guy that was up for the challenge. One of the best that ever did it was the woman who birthed me, Koo-Koo.

Now Koo-Koo was a story within herself, a real urban book. The name should speak for itself because my mom was crazy. I am almost positive she should have been born a guy because she did it all just like a guy. She made her mark in plenty of hoods throughout the city. See, because I had two grandmothers in the same area, my mom would be back and forth between Bonnie Doone and Shaw Road doing her thing. She sold it all too! Weed, crack, powder, dope—it didn't make a difference! Koo-Koo's motto was, *anything will sell, but nothing won't.* Because of Koo-Koo, my hustlers' mentality was already implanted in my brain from birth. Just like sickle cell, being a hustler is hereditary. It's passed down from generation to generation. It's in the bloodline. My mom was bred, as far as hustlers go. She dedicated her every waking moment to running up a dollar. Little did I know, the apple wouldn't fall far from the tree.

It all started out with me being observant. Oh, I didn't miss much. Even from an early age. I didn't let shit get past me. I loved watching the hood come to life. I loved seeing it wake up from its slumber. Haymount Hill was an energy all in itself. It kept something going to feed my curious mind. Instead of eating Gerber baby food as a child, I consumed the scraps of game that fell off Haymount Hill's table of hustlers, starting with my grandmother.

My grandmother sold candy apples to all the hustlers in and around the hood. Fascinated, I'd see them pull out wads of money so they could pay her. I was always mesmerized with the night life. Well, as much as I could see of it anyway; my grandmother made sure I came in before the street lights came on. My little nosey ass was in that house, and all I could do is stare out of the window, hoping I could be a part of the hustle and bustle of Clark Street.

I remember one day my grandmother and I were sitting on the front porch. The sun was shining, the summer had just kicked in full swing. I had my eyes glued to the things going on in the street, and my mind was a million miles and running. I saw a few guys walking, looking rough. It was like they knew I was watching so they put a little extra swag in their steps. I was so captivated by the performance I didn't even hear my grandmother calling me. It was as if I was underwater, she seem so far away.

"Larry!" She finally said loud enough to bring me back from wherever I'd drifted off too.

Slowly, I turned toward her, the guys I wanted to be like still in my line of sight. Half of my attention was concerned about what she was trying to say, the other half was across the street with those guys, talking whatever kind of talk they talked, sagging their pants, and just being cool.

"Yes ma'am?" I whispered, still focused on my idols, whoever they were.

"I asked you what you wanted to be when you grow up." She said with an edge to her voice. "Do you know?"

I nodded my head, still focused on my role models across the street.

"Ok, so what is it?"

I am sure she thought I was going to say a policeman or a fireman, or something like that. Something that would let her know that she was raising me the right way. A God-fearing way. I wanted to tell her that I wanted to be one of those things she probably wanted me to be, something she considered honorable. I wanted to set her loving heart at ease, but I also wanted to always do my best to tell her the truth. And I did that day. Slowly, I raised my hand and pointed to the guys standing across the street.

"I want to be like them," I announced confidently, my skinny little arm extended in the direction of those boys.

My grandmother's beautiful face turned into a mask of anger, hurt, and something else I couldn't quite put my hands on. I felt the slap well before it hit my face. I don't know how or why, but that was one for the history books. I am willing to bet she'd practiced that swing a time or two. When her palm connected with my face, I immediately saw stars, and those little birds that the cartoon characters see when they get smacked by a train or something. (Ole' May Small had a right hook from hell back then. LOL.)

"Don't you ever, and I mean *ever* let me hear you say you want to be like those little hoodlums!" She hissed with venom dripping from every word. My cheeks stung like a thousand bees had given me the business. My cheeks hurt so bad I couldn't even say, *Ouch,* because it hurt way more than an *Ouch*. It was more like a *Daaaaamn,* but I wasn't about to curse because my jaw would've been broken instead of stinging. I could literally see fire in my grandmother's eyes, along with mist from the trail of tears beginning to form in her eyes.

"Let me tell you something," my grandmother continued. "I've seen too many of our people brought down in the streets, Larry. I can count on my hands how many men have died or gone to jail for the rest of their life trying to catch a dollar that can never truly be caught. Now, I am sorry if I hurt you, but I am not sorry I hit you, because I hope and pray that it served its purpose. Now go in the house, you've seen enough for one day."

I slowly crawled to my feet, still not trusting my balance, and tried to walk. I stopped for a second to gather my bearings, and to get one last glimpse of the guys that got me slapped in the first place. See, what my grandmother didn't know, I was already forming a plan in my preteen head. I'd already set the wheels in motion, and I'd already committed to who I wanted to be. My life was already written before it ever started, and it was about time I started living it because God only gave me one, so I might as well give it all I got, I figured.

Grandma there's no doubt you raised me the right way with your teachings. Every week, Wednesday, Friday, and Sunday, you had me in church. I guess the best way to explain the way I turned out is that some things are destined, and it was destined for me to be a street nigga.

My Block

CHAPTER 3
Meet the Streets

Ok, now I'm 13-years-old and I feel like it's time to be a man. The saying that, '*when life throws you lemons, make lemonade*' is true, but for me I took that shit a little further and I made my own lemon tree. Shit, why make lemonade for a day, when I can make it for a lifetime?

Things were going crazy around grandma's house. My granddad was still trippin, aunts and cousins were still going in on me every chance they got. So, I did what any self-respecting 13-year-old would do. I got the hell out of dodge. There was no other way I saw it to be.

Hell, my grandmother was outnumbered with the get-rid-of-him vote, and although I'm almost positive she would have fought to her last breath for me, I chose to save her the ridicule and bounced. Shit, I had no plans to stay where I'm not wanted. It was a new me. I'd watched and watched and learned everything I could by observation. Now, it was time for some hands-on training. Hell, I didn't have any other choice anyway. It was either get to this bag or end up in one from starvation. Failure wasn't even an option in my book.

I remember when I first made up my mind that it was the day to venture out on my own and proclaim my manhood. I went to see a guy that I thought would get me on my feet. His name was Big June, and he was the guy that sold me my first double up, two-for-twenty. I thought I had something, but later found out that it was only bread. Big June had shitted me. Or so he thought. Early on in life, I knew that if I didn't stand for something, I'd fall for anything. And what better time than now to start standing? I threw that shit he sold me down for the birds to eat, and I went and stole my uncle Ant Lee's gun. I tracked Big June down and unloaded that thirty-eight at his big ass. I missed him, but I got my point across because he never crossed me again. Thus, started the growth of the man you know today. (R.I.P Big June. He was gunned down by the police in the early 2000's.)

After busting at Big June, it was like the whole neighborhood knew that I had a gun, even my grandmother. She would ride through the hood looking for me, asking people if they'd seen me anywhere. I would see her first though and hide in the woods while she rode by. Because, besides God, she was the only thing I feared.

The first time I ever touched real drugs, it was given to me from my mother, Koo-Koo. Yep, my mother gave me my first pack. I remember she was going with this guy named Baby Boy from Shaw Road. (My mom migrated over there when I was born. I guess she was trying to expand her criminal enterprise.) She gave me about seven rocks and told me to bring her back a certain amount of money. The crazy part about this is, I've never seen nor interacted with the woman who brought me into this world until I entered her world. That was folly on her part, though, because had she known me, she would've known I wasn't into bringing anything back. Shit, I was spending the nights riding around in crackhead cars and getting my dick sucked by crackhead women who would do anything for one or two of those little rocks. No way was I about to bring her shit back off those seven rocks. As soon as they dropped in my hand, I already knew which crackhead I was going to get to suck my dick for them. That was around the time I found out the power behind those little white pieces of cocaine. I was the wrong one to let find out that on my block I was *him* as long as I had some work. My whole life was dedicated to becoming *him* and staying *him.* Every move was a calculated step.

Now don't get me wrong, I had friends (or associates), but they were all in the same life as me. Only one of them was a regular dude. Well, at least back then he was. His name was Jesse "Jig" Johnson. Jesse was one of my best friends, but my homies that were already in the streets were: Lil' Kev (K-Kutta), Meat-Meat aka Monkey Brains, and Jada.

Jada's mother's house was the spot where we *got to it*. Her name was Mrs. Helen, and she was on drugs too. I remember seeing Jada sell his mom some crack one day. Seeing him do that sparked something in me. It bothered me so much I had to ask him, how could he sell his mom crack?

Jada looked at me, his dark skin shining in the light, and asked, "What?" He was so offended his voice went deep. "What did you say man?"

I'd always been fearless, so a deep voice and sharp eyes were far from something that could scare me away. I dropped the tone in my voice to match his and repeated my question, "I said, how can you sell your mom crack?"

He pressed pause on the video game we were playing and turned toward me. "You serious, Long?" He asked.

"I asked it, didn't I?" I responded.

He got up and grabbed my arm. He pulled me to the kitchen then let my arm go so he could open the refrigerator. As soon as the door swung open, I knew what he was going to say, but I kept my mouth closed so he could answer my question his way.

"This is why, Long. I'd rather her spend her money with me than with them," he said with emotion leaking from every word. "This is why I sell that shit to my mom. So, me and my little brother can eat. Terrance shouldn't have to starve because his mom can't stop smoking long enough to feed her own damn kids."

That was all he had to say. I got the picture loud and clear, and I learned a valuable lesson that day from my homie.

Years later, Jada was gunned down on Davis Street trying to be the man I always knew him to be. He was trying to save one of the little McNeil girls from getting shot and sacrificed his own life in the process. *Damn, I miss you boy!*

Shout out to Mrs. Helen. If you're reading this, know that you are appreciated. I know there is nothing I can say to bring him back. Also, know that I'll always be grateful for all the times you hid us from the cops, and gave us your knowledge and support throughout the years. Most importantly, big ups to you for kicking your crack habit. I love you baby!

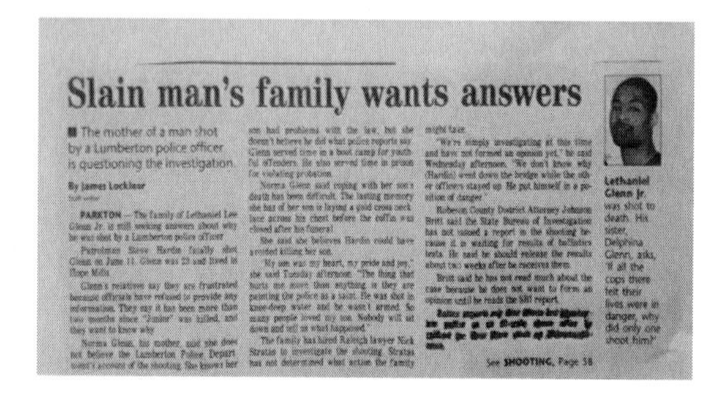

Slain man's family wants answers

■ The mother of a man shot by a Lumberton police officer is questioning the investigation.

By James Locklear
Staff writer

PARKTON — The family of Lethaniel Lee Glenn Jr. is still seeking answers about why he was shot by a Lumberton police officer.

Patrolman Steve Hardin fatally shot Glenn on June 11. Glenn was 23 and lived in Hope Mills.

Glenn's relatives say they are frustrated because officials have refused to provide any information. They say it has been more than two months since "Junior" was killed, and they want to know why.

Norma Glenn, his mother, said she does not believe the Lumberton Police Department's account of the shooting. She knows her son had problems with the law, but she doesn't believe he did what police reports say. Glenn served time in a boot camp for youthful offenders. He also served time in prison for violating probation.

Norma Glenn said coping with her son's death has been difficult. The lasting memory she has of her son is laying a gold cross necklace across his chest before the coffin was closed after his funeral.

She said she believes Hardin could have avoided killing her son.

"My son was my heart, my pride and joy," she said Tuesday afternoon. "The thing that hurts me more than anything is they are painting the police as a saint. He was shot in knee-deep water and he wasn't armed. So many people loved my son. Nobody will sit down and tell us what happened."

The family has hired Raleigh lawyer Nick Stratas to investigate the shooting. Stratas has not determined what action the family might take.

"We're simply investigating at this time and have not formed an opinion yet," he said Wednesday afternoon. "We don't know why (Hardin) went down the bridge while the other officers stayed up. He put himself in a position of danger."

Robeson County District Attorney Johnson Britt said the State Bureau of Investigation has not issued a report in the shooting because it is waiting for results of ballistics tests. He said he should release the results about two weeks after he receives them.

Britt said he has not read much about the case because he does not want to form an opinion until he reads the SBI report.

[illegible]

See **SHOOTING**, Page 5B

Lethaniel Glenn Jr. was shot to death. His sister, Delphina Glenn, asks, "If all the cops there felt their lives were in danger, why did only one shoot him?"

Big June's Death

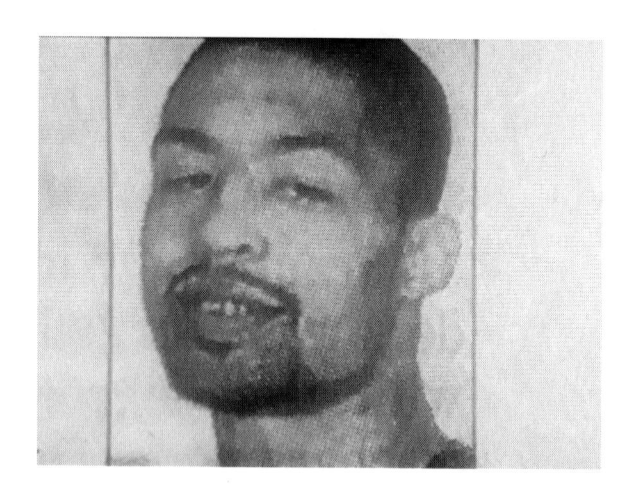

Big June

R.I.P. Jada

Ms. Helen

CHAPTER 4
Droppin' Jewels

Every major figure started off in their do-boy stage. Even me, even little Larry Longhead. See, every great leader had to have been a great follower first. That's just the rules. You cut your teeth at leadership, learning the ins and outs, by being a follower of other leaders. Me, Lil' Kev, and Meat-Meat were no different. We hung around all the hustlers. We made runs for whatever they were willing to give us. Of course, they paid us for running errands, but the thing we traded our services for most was the knowledge they dropped on us daily. Like sponges, we soaked up every piece of the game that was bestowed on us. So, in hindsight, it was an even swap. If I knew what I know now, I would have spent a little more time with those older guys because the jewels they gave us were priceless.

We were wild with youth at the time, and loyal to those that were loyal to us. We stood by each other's side, no matter what. One for all, and all for one. Kev was driving cars at 9-years-old. No, I'm serious, 9-years-old! I remember Kev used to get people to take him to the store, and when the car pulled up to the store, he'd put on that innocent face and ask the person to go into the store to buy him blunts. Kev would then pull off and come pick me up. Then, we'd go pick up Meat and joyride all day while Meat searched their shit like he owned it.

I swear, I can't make this shit up… (LOL.) My lil' crew was really about that life! Oh, I was still homeless, but now I was learning the game, day by day. It was just hard being a match and hanging out with the dynamite who was Kev. We needed some balance; the life was off-the-chain at an early age. Driving, tricking, pulling all-nighters, and flipping our little money. My crew was my crew, and I'm sure I could write a whole book on just our episodes alone, but I'll keep it short and sweet for now.

I remember one time we were on the block with the OG's and my uncle Kojack came up in his car. He leaned out the window with a bag of weed dangling between his fingers.

"Come here, Long," he said. "What you and Lil' Kev doing?"

"Nothing," I replied, holding on to the door, hypnotized by the bag of weed. My mouth was watering with desire. "What's up?" I asked.

My uncle Kojack was crazy, but we was about that shit too. Kev came over and he didn't even ask any questions. He immediately jumped in the back seat and I followed suit.

"Y'all trying to blow some of this here, lil' niggas?" Uncle Kojack asked while pulling off from the curb. "I'm about to show y'all what real weed do. Not that bullshit y'all be smoking," he promised.

I turned up the music and let it flow through the speakers. I could see Kev in the backseat bobbing his head. We were in the mix. I had no idea where Kojack was taking us. All I know is after about ten minutes, he stopped the car. That's when I made the choice to look around. It wasn't like I really gave a damn anyway, shit. I was trying to get my lungs dirty and go to the moon.

From my first glance, I could tell that we were in the back of some type of house or building. The moon was bright this night for some reason. I remember looking up and thinking that this would be the perfect night for werewolves.

"Y'all get out," Kojack instructed, opening the door. I noticed the overhead light didn't come on when he opened the door. I thought that to be strange, but it was only a passing thought, being as though I wanted so badly to see what kind of weed he had. Kev hopped out of the backseat and came around to sit on the hood beside me. Kojack stood in front of us. He dipped in his front pocket, took out a Philly blunt, and passed it to me.

"Split that," he said to me. Then he gave Kev the weed rolled inside a bill and told him to break it up.

We both focused on the task of preparing the weed and got lost in our mission. So, when I heard the sliding of the chamber, and the bullet going into the head, my heart dropped to my knees. The sound was unmistakable to both of our young ears.

Slowly, I raised my head. I could see Kev out the corner of my eye doing the same thing. When I looked up, my eyes immediately caught the gleam of a nickel-plated pistol. I had no idea what we'd done to Kojack, but I knew that whatever it was, he didn't come to play any games.

I remember thinking about something one of the OG's said on the block one day, ***'I would rather die like a man, than live like a coward...'*** he had boldly proclaimed. I don't know why I thought of his words at that moment. They resonated deep within me, strong and powerful, and it was the mantra I decided to live (or die) with. Kev must have felt me too because he gave Kojack his undivided attention with an unflinching stare. Kojack didn't have the gun pointed at us, it was hanging in his right hand with the barrel toward the ground.

I spoke first, "What's this about, Yack?" I asked him. "What you on?"

His head was down as if he was in deep thought. In my mind, he was thinking about killing us and where to bury the bodies. He looked up, and when his eyes met mine, I wanted to try him, but I knew this nigga was on one, so I fell back.

"Y'all wanna know what this about, right?" Kojack whispered menacingly.

"Damn right!" Kev said with the dollar bill full of broken down weed in his hand.

"This is about the both of you two lil' niggas and knowing who the fuck you are."

"Huh?" We said in unison. We were utterly confused now.

Kojack held the gun up and yanked the slide back. A bullet popped out, and he caught it in the air. Then, he tucked the gun back in his pants and both of our heartbeats slowed down. I even sent up a little prayer to the man upstairs for granting us mercy and sparing our lives. I still didn't know what Kojack had planned, but I didn't think our immediate deaths were in the cards anymore.

Kojack stared both of us down. The moon was so bright, I could see it reflecting off the whites of his eyes. Everything seemed to be intensified. I even smelled the potent weed in Kev's hand.

"I want y'all to listen and listen real good," Kojack said. "Never let the little picture blind you from the big picture. See how easy it was for me to get both of you in the car and out here in the dark? All it took was a promise of a high! This weed could've been fake. I could've sold you a dream and you would have been dead, left behind this house. They wouldn't have found your bodies for months," he estimated. Kev and I was tuned in because we both knew he was kicking some true shit. Kojack was as official as they came, so his game was too.

"What both of you have to remember is, it ain't no guarantees in this life. You could be here today and gone tomorrow! These clowns out here got kicked out the circus, so they found a new spot to do their tricks," he informed us. "See, the difference between them and y'all is, y'all don't mind going to get what you want. These fake dudes hide behind the image and names of real niggas. Never let a man ride the wave of your name, because your name is all you got at times," he schooled, then looked at Kev. "Nigga roll up, what y'all gonna do? Look at the weed? Put that shit in the air!"

"Oh, my bad," I said, grabbing the bill from Kev and rolling up while Kojack continued.

"Check this out... never trust a bitch. Never let the pussy cloud your judgment. When you're looking at the small picture of getting your dick wet, the bigger picture is this bitch could be setting you up, trying to fuck you to get her a name, or out for your money. It's a lot dealing with them hoes; don't ever trust them once a month bleeding bitches. Never let a nigga cross you or play you either, because if you open that door, it'll never close. You must love yourself more than anybody loves you. If anybody tries to handle you on any level–even me, I'm not an exception to the rule either–no matter who it is, you deal with them. Even if it's your daddy. Fuck him too! Now let's get the fuck out of here so I can do what I do."

Shout out to my uncle Kojack. Yack, if you're reading this, I want you to know I never met nothing like you. You take the good with the bad. Just like you give it to dudes, you take it. You've been shot 21 times all together. Last time I spoke to you, you told me you was trying to get your health back up.

Yack, this game you gave me was almost 20 years ago, and it stuck with me and helped me out through the years. I really appreciate you, from the heart.

Kojack went right instead of left when the Feds stepped in.

My Uncle Kojack

CHAPTER 5

Be Careful Who You Approach

They say there is a lesson in everything–even a bullet, if you catch it right. After the jewels dropped by Kojack, I continued to soak up game from Kojack and Mo. Mo was this guy who got high, but he had a brilliant mind. I had no choice but to respect his mind. Shit, he gave the game to the dudes who gave the game to the dudes who gave the game to me.

Me, Kev, and Meat were still on the same move, doing shit we do. We were just a little bit more cautious, considering we knew all about the motives of men now, thanks to the game we were learning.

See, knowing is really half the battle. The other half is action. Unfortunately, around this time, we were still kids, still wild, and still ready for anything that came our way. Being young and wild I was still moving in the circles of my age group.

I attended Douglas Byrd Middle School. It was a predominantly black school full of young, fly kids trying to make their way in life. I went to school, but barely. I was 80 percent in the streets, and 20 percent in school. So, I'll say school was not my favorite place, except for the bitches. Now that was my favorite subject.

I was on my game when it came to the hoes. I was always fresh to death with the latest shoes or outfit that came out at that time. I'd always been a fool about my money, my clothes, and my grandmother. Even to this day, I'm still the same man, but back then if I saw it, I went for it.

Like Jolina ... now that was a fish worth catching.

Jolina was one of the baddest bitches in school. She was mixed, Guam and Caucasian, and was *tough*! I'm talking flawless. If I could go back in time to relive the moments with her, I would. She was that damn pretty, easily the Top 5 in the whole school. I remember the first time I laid eyes on her. She was walking down the hall, glowing like an angel. I couldn't tear my eyes away from her. I made up my mind right then and there that I had to have her. I *had* to shoot my shot. Man, I'm from Haymount Hill; ain't no hoes this way. We go get what we want, and that's that on that. So, I shot Jolina a note, telling her that I wanted her to be my girl. She blushed and wrote me right back. Her answer was, *yes*! That was the start of the flyest couple at Douglas Byrd.

Me and Jolina would stay on the phone for hours chopping it up about everything under the sun. I can't lie, I was digging shorty for a minute.

They lived in a neighborhood behind the middle school we went to. One day I went to her house and she introduced me to her mom. Her mom was a white lady and her daddy was a Guam. I had to give them their props, they made a hell of a baby because Jolina was a bad bitch.

I remember one day she and I skipped school and went to her house. She didn't know it, but I already had it in my mind that I was going for the gold that day. I was a little shocked at first because I wasn't trying to get caught up in her house slipping. I didn't have my strap, so I was extra cautious. Jolina took me up to her room and we got undressed. My heart was pounding a million beats per second as we started to get busy. I got on top. Jolina told me she was a virgin, so I did my best to take my time when what I really wanted to do was stick it in and jackrabbit my way to my nut. Unfortunately, she started crying as soon as I put it in. She said it hurt too bad. I didn't get no pleasure from seeing her cry, so I slowed down and made it work for both of us. Sadly, it didn't last long, but after it was done we were both head over heels in love. Or so we thought. Her mom would try to come between us, but Jolina wasn't trying to hear none of that shit. My girl had my back.

One day I was in school selling my weed, and I let Jolina hold it in her locker. I'd get what I needed to sell between periods, then keep the rest inside her locker. Jolina told one of her friends that she had my weed in her locker (I don't know what the hell she was thinking.) The friend told the school police that Jolina had something in her locker. Next thing you know, the school detention officer went and bagged Jolina. They took her and the weed to the principal's office where they called her mom up to the school. I had no idea what the fuck was going on until they called me up there.

When I came in the door, before I could say a word, Jolina's mom started screaming about how I was going to ruin her daughter's life. She yelled that I was a criminal, and a drug dealer. I tried to gather where all this heat was coming from and why she was coming at me like that. Meanwhile, the police tried to calm her down. See, I didn't know what was going on until I saw Jolina in the principal's office with handcuffs on.

They asked me if I knew anything, and I quickly said, "No." *These clowns can't know where I'm from,* I thought to myself.

After I told them I didn't know anything, they hauled Jolina's ass up out that bitch and took her ass to Juvie.

We didn't let that stop us though. We kept in touch through her best friend, Kamisha. After the incident, they kicked me out of school too, but the crazy part about it was they messed around and sent us to the same alternative school. Ain't that some shit? (LOL.) So, it was back on before they could cut it off.

Jolina stood tall for me that day at the school, and I'll always give her the props she deserves for being a solid chick in this watered-down world.

Back then, Jolina was hanging out with this chick named Nicole. Nicole wasn't as pretty as Jolina. She was cute, so I put her down with my homie Jada's little brother, Terrance. We'd all skip school together, turn up, and fuck in abandoned houses. One day, shit got out of hand. It was definitely a day I know I'll remember for the rest of my life. I believe some things are meant to be remembered, and some are not. This was one of those days and events that will forever be burned in my mind.

Jolina, Nicole, and I skipped school. We went to my other grandmother's house, Ann–Koo-Koo's mom. They let me do what I wanted to do over there. While we smoked a blunt, Jolina was on my left while Nicole was on my right. I had my pack in my hand, about 15 rocks. I sat them down so I could fuck with Jolina, and Nicole spoke out of the blue!

"Ohh, let me have one of those!" she said, with a gleam in her eyes.

Immediately I looked over my shoulder at her. "Girl, you trippin'. You don't know what the fuck that is. That's crack."

She looked at me like I was stupid. Her head tilted to the side, she said, "Boy, I know what it is. I've smoked some before. That ain't nothing new."

"Girl, that ain't nothing to play with," I warned, untangling myself from Jolina. "That's money right there. That's how I get my paper."

"Boy, I know," she insisted. "I told you, I done did it before. Plus, I only want one of them."

I studied her for a little while. Her eyes kept going from my face to the bag on the table. If I was thinking back then, I mean *really* thinking, I would have known right then because I would have asked the right questions. But I was a kid, and Jolina's pretty ass was on my mind. At that exact moment, I was willing to do anything just to shut her ass up.

"Do you know how to smoke it?" I asked getting up off the couch, Jolina's pretty ass looking up at me. I looked back down at her. "Has she ever smoked crack before?"

Jolina's shrugged her shoulders, not even trying to concern herself with our foolishness. I didn't even wait for a reply from either of them. I took it upon myself to go outside and grab a can, so I could make her a pipe. See, where I'm from, we learn early in the game that knowledge is power and knowing how to assist a smoker with the utensils can be extremely profitable. I could do all types of things with little or nothing.

So, I grabbed the first can I saw. (Of course, I was a little impatient, because I could've been in the house loving all on Jolina.) I took it back in the house and they were sitting in the same spots. I poked big holes in it so she could get the maximum smoke from her toke. She looked like she was about to jump on me before I could get it finished. I took the ashtray that had the ashes from the blunt we smoked still in it. I dumped it on top, took out one of the rocks from my pack and set it on top of the can. Nicole leaned into me and I gave her the can. She got up and took it in the bathroom with her. She stayed in there for almost 20 minutes before coming out. While she was in the bathroom getting high, I took that time to play my hand with Jolina. Eventually, Nicole returned from the bathroom and joined us. She sat down and we chilled until it was time for us to go because school was out. When it was time for them to get dropped off in their neighborhood, Nicole burst out crying, screaming, "Don't nobody love me!"

Panicked, Jolina said to me, "What did you do to my friend? What's wrong with her?"

That shit fucked me up, but I was a G; my mind was already working. I walked over to her and whispered in her ear, "If you stop crying, I'll give you another one."

This wasn't my first rodeo, I'd seen this move a thousand times before, just not with a girl so young. Yet and still it worked, because she instantly stopped crying. I took that time to get them the fuck out of my grandma Ann's house.

After that incident, Nicole got turned all the way out and got on all types of drugs. (R.I.P. Nicole. She died from a heroin overdose. I feel I'm part to blame for ever giving you that shit, starting you off. I was only a kid myself, unaware. I apologize to Nicole's family. God forgave me. I forgave me. I just hope y'all find it in your heart to forgive me as well.)

Dealing with Jolina was cool, but along with the up's, there were some down's too. Like having one of the baddest broads brought all types of envy and jealousy out of niggas in the school.

One day, Jolina, Terrance, Nicole, and I was in her neighborhood getting high, smoking a few blunts. When we were done, we started walking through her neighborhood. After a few minutes, about five guys came up and surrounded us. The one who dubbed himself the leader spoke first,

"Yo, y'all in the wrong neighborhood. Y'all bout to get fucked up," he claimed.

Now, my gangster was on out the gate, but before I could speak a word, Jolina started going in.

"Motherfucka they with me. Y'all ain't 'bout to do shit!" Jolina screamed.

Shit, she almost scared me. They started to say something but went ahead and walked way. Terrance was hot. I was cool. He wanted to go grab some straps and come back. I ignored him and turned to Jolina.

"Who was the dark skinned skinny dude?" I asked calmly.

"They ain't worth it, Long," she said looking into my eyes. "They weren't about to do anything."

"Oh, I know that," I shot back. "I just wanna know who they are." My tone was as disarming as I could get it. We all looked on until they faded in the distance.

Jolina knew I was waiting on an answer, so she gave me one, "His name is Jamal. He ain't no-damn-body."

"Oh, he is somebody," I said with fire in my eyes. "He is somebody to me, because I'm gonna get that motherfucker."

See, I've always been the one to give the rope so people could hang themselves. Also, I've always been a finisher. I don't start it all, but I finish everything.

About two months passed by without me ever seeing any of those dudes who I felt tried to test my gangster that day, but even a ground hog sees his shadow once a year.

One night, Douglas Byrd had a football game, and if you're from Fayetteville, then you know that Douglas Byrd High School games was the place to be at our age. Everybody who was anybody was there, and even a few nobody's. I went out there dolo, but I ran into a few homies I knew, Taylor and Corey. They had a few guys with them, and we were all on the hunt for some bitches. As luck would have it, I spotted Jamal. As soon as I saw Jamal, I immediately canceled out looking for bitches. My focus was on Jamal. I told Corey and Taylor that I was going to get that nigga, and they didn't hesitate for a second.

"Let's get 'em!" They both said.

I watched him for the rest of the night until he walked away from the crowd. I really didn't give a damn if Corey and Taylor were with me or not, I had a mission to accomplish. Just before I made my move, I told them.

I blew down on him with only him on my mind. The crazy ass shit was, all his whole crew took off running in different directions. Now, I told you, I give props where they're do, and I gotta give Jamal his. When his homies ran, he stayed right there. He showed heart. It was misplaced, but still he had it, when his bitch-ass homies turned into greyhounds. In my opinion, maybe he should have ran, because as soon as I said, "What's up now, you bitch-ass nigga?" I took off on him and my crew followed suit.

We beat that boy like he stole something. I'm talking, guns and bricks to the head for at least five minutes. The only reason we stopped was because someone screamed that he was dead. That was all it took for us to get the fuck out of dodge. Jamal was fucked all the way up. He stayed in a coma for a long time after that. NO ONE knew who did it until Jamal came out of the coma and identified me. I ended up in training school for the beatdown. They hit me with attempted murder. Only me though; I took the rap. A true G until the end.

Jamal, if you're reading this, my advice to you homie is: be careful who you approach in life because you never know what a person been through, or what they got on their plate. Live and let live homie.

I've seen Jamal numerous times after this. I would say we have a mutual understanding: don't jump into my lane and I won't fuck you up.

CHAPTER 6
Timmy's Lesson

I want everyone to know that the angle I'm taking for this book is mine. So, it's unapologetic and as straight forwards as it's going to get. I won't make excuses for anything I say in this book because the thing about having an explanation for whatever I say is: my friends don't need excuses, and my enemies don't want them. If you're neutral, then you'll be okay anyway, because it is what it is. Just sit back and enjoy, because I'm about to take it there.

Now, I'm 16 and out of training school. I don't know what training school was supposed to train me, or if it was supposed to train me anything. Oh, I learned a lot, but I'm positive it wasn't what they meant for me to learn. Like, how to be a better criminal or how to put the fear of God in the hearts of suckers. Yeah, I learned all that and more. And now that I'm home, I planned on putting all that knowledge and pent-up frustration to good use.

As soon as I got to the city, K-Kutta (Lil' Kev) and I jumped right back in the mix. Now our young names floated on waves of respect. It was always whatever with us. We held no cut cards. The lessons that Kojack taught us was set in stone. We knew at least 80 percent of nigga's getting money in our city was soft. 10 percent was getting so much money, they'd already put their guns down, and the last 10 percent knew we were ready to die just like them, so they left us the fuck alone. Bottom line–and there is always a bottom line–in this case, you had to respect heat-holders. And that was us to the fullest.

I can't say that we were these invincible serial killers, because we weren't. We were just ready to come for whoever sent for us. Fear is a by-product of the weak. I'm sure Koo-Koo and Longhead didn't wait nine months for a boy that was a bitch on the inside. I knew where I was at, so I adapted to my environment. They don't call the city *Fayettenam* for nothing. Shit really hits the fan out this bitch. I was just good at making sure it didn't blow back on me.

Me and the homies still did things boys our age did. We hung out at each other's house, played the game when we could, chased girls every chance we got, and got high, but we were really grown men in the making. We were soaking up every ounce of the game that we could from the OG's around our way.

Being a police officer or an astronaut was never something I aspired to be. I always knew I had to be one of the best hustlers and gun busters that my city ever saw. Legends are born in the depths of adversity, and I'm no different. There was no other way to be. In this jungle where I'm from, either you're one of the kings or your ass better stay out of the way. It was always someone out there that thought they were tougher than me, and I'm sure it was. I just haven't met him yet. If I do, I'm sure one of us will have to die that day.

I remember a time I was at Reggie's Liquor house on Davis Street. It was around two in the morning. A few chicks and I were playing a game of spades while Reggie made his change off his shots. I was chilling this night, not bothering anybody, just being easy. The door opened, and someone came in. I'm not even checking for who it is, because I really didn't give a damn. My back is to the door anyway, plus I gotta watch these sneaky-ass bitches. They might try to cheat me.

"Long, let me holla at you," a voice says behind my back. I slowly turned around and saw Timmy. Timmy was about his change around that time, so he held some respect in the hood. I'd never had any problems with homie, so I didn't think too much into him calling me outside.

I put my cards down and followed him outside. As soon as we cleared the door, he started going in on me,

"What the fuck you doing here?" He said loud enough for everybody to hear. "I'm gonna say this once, man: you need to get the fuck out of here before I do something bad to you, lil' nigga."

I had no idea what the hell he was talking about, but I could see in his eyes that he was on one. He was looking at me waiting for a response. He didn't get one. I just left. I took off down the street without another word. I could feel the eyes on my back, Timmy's and the girls' I was playing spades with. They had come outside trying to calm him down. It was all good.

I kept walking until I made it to my stash spot. I grabbed what I needed and within 10 minutes I was back at Reggie's, but this time I wasn't by myself. I walked in and saw that nigga Timmy playing cards with the same bitches, sitting in my same spot. Damn! I didn't know what the fuck was going on with this dude! If he wanted to play that damn bad, all he had to do is call next! *This nigga done went crazy,* I thought. He didn't even turn around or anything, he just kept on playing.

Well, I'm sure that this was going to be the most expensive spades game Timmy would ever play.

When I got within a foot of his punk ass, I let him meet my friend that I brought back with me. I took that .45 and introduced it to Timmy's head. I pistol whipped his ass like he deserved. The girls went screaming in different directions, frantic out of their minds. I'm sure they weren't used to the type of violence I was putting out. I was swinging that .45, going for broke on his ass. As soon as I thought about putting a couple rounds in his ass to really teach him a lesson, Reggie came running out the back and begged me not to do that shit in his spot. I fucked with Reggie back then, so I left Timmy's ass right there on the floor leaking.

I went outside because my adrenaline was pumping through my veins. I wanted to body something! The girls followed me outside telling me how crazy I was and succeeded at calming me down.

After about ten or fifteen minutes, I tucked the pistol and was about to leave when Timmy stumbled outside, clothes soaked in blood, holding his head where I split his ass. I don't know what he was thinking because I was thinking we're even. He tried to play me in front of everybody, and I came back and gave his ass the business. In my world, an even swap ain't no damn swindle.

We both caught eye contact and I let my hand drift toward my pistol, just in case he had one on him now. Instead of pulling out a piece, he spoke,

"That's how you do it, lil' nigga," he said, still holding his head, blood oozing between his fingers. "That's how you handle your business. But let me tell you something, don't ever, for as long as you live, pull a gun on anybody and not use it."

I was almost positive that this wasn't a time to be dropping jewels or teaching life lessons. Even still, who was I to question a man's timing? Like I said, I was a sponge. So, I picked up exactly what Timmy was putting down.

I looked him dead in the eye and told him, "You're right." Then I pulled out the same .45 I just whipped him with and wet his ass up.

Timmy wasn't my first shooting victim, and far from my last. Timmy was just the only one to teach me a lesson and get that same lesson taught to his ass.

Hey you, Timmy, if you reading this, I know we haven't spoken since then. I just want you to know the lesson you taught me. That night is a part of what made me legendary in the city. I ain't ever pull it out again unless I was gonna use it. So, good looking on that. I wish you and your family the best. Just don't ever cross me, homie, and we won't have to go through that again.

CHAPTER 7
Intruding Territory

I'm willing to bet that people without a name in the streets have no idea how much work it takes to hold that name up in them same streets that gave it to you in the first place. See, a name is made early, and as time goes on, stories are built around that name and it becomes an entity within itself. Like smelling smoke before you see the fire, the smoke should deter you from fucking with the fire. You should already know that fire comes in and turns shit into ashes. But some people don't learn. They just got to see for themselves if the fire is as big and hot as they think, or as they heard it is.

See, I'm that fire behind the smoke. If some people would have been as smart as they claim to be, they would've paid attention to the smoke and got the fuck out the building. Some did, some didn't. The ones that did, I salute. The ones that didn't well, let's just say we both know how that went. I said before that I'm not this sociopathic serial killer. I'm almost positive that a lot of the stories about me are some bullshit made up by the police or hating ass clowns that sit around the card table drinking 40's and cheap liquor. I've done my share of dirt. Shit, if I didn't have a story to tell I wouldn't be writing this book, now would I?

As I was saying, holding that name up takes work, especially when you really are the nigga you think you are. You do what you want when you want, at whatever cost.

I remember Kev and I decided to branch out from our normal spot. We were always looking for a new adventure. I think we both might have had A.D.H.D. back then because we decided we could hit Nimmocks. Everybody called it 'down the way'. We heard that money was running in that area, and us being who we were, went to see 'bout that change A.S.A.P. True to talk, it was money coming through like that. See, we made it a thing for us to go down the way and get some of their money too.

We started posting on a regular basis. We'd be in the woods and paths like we were from there. We were going where the money was at. It was like *Pokémon Go* out that bitch, but instead of chasing those little monsters, we were chasing the almighty dollar. After a little while we even had our own smoker from their area. Her name was Shondella. She would help us get to it all night long.

We did it all, even started renting their smoker-cars. It was like, 'fuck it,' go hard or go the fuck home. I can't say that we just took all the way over, because we didn't. We were just getting a piece of 'Down the Way' pie.

It was some movers and shakers on that side too. It was a dude named BK who was running it up at that time. Now in my opinion, BK was soft. To others, he might have been a gangster God, but to me, homie wasn't him. I know a lot of tough niggas, and he ain't one of them. I held no respect for him. I did hold respect for the two lil' niggas that he ran with, Cognac and Lil Whodie. Those two niggas was 'bout that shit. Like I said, heat holders respect heat holders. Even still, they could have never came to Haymount Hill and did the shit we did. Hell-to-the-no!!! Shit would have been lit as soon as we spotted them. (I'm just saying.) We knew they didn't want us over there doing what we do, taking food out of their mouths. We heard whispers, niggas hating, but we were always on point. Ready for war, if that's what they wanted to bring, especially with that nigga, BK. Kev nor I liked that dude. It was to the point that he didn't have to jump out there but an inch, and we'd take the mile.

We had built up this huge dislike for dude that would only be quenched by some type of action. So, the day we were in that area driving one of their rental cars, we had our chance. By the luck of the draw, this nigga BK pulled up to the same light that stopped us. Kev noticed him first.

"There go that bitch ass nigga right there, bro," Kev said without turning his head too much to give us away.

"Shol' is," I said, my hand already itching for the feel of my pistol. "Shit, what's up? I don't give a fuck about the daylight."

"Me either," Kev said, reaching for his piece as I reached for mine.

Before the window could roll down good we were letting that nigga have it. I'm sure the people all around had no idea what the fuck was going on. I didn't give a damn if they did. I was trying to get my man, hell or high water. Sad to say, we still missed his punk ass. BK must have had an angel on his side because he ducked every bit of that work. Still, the streets got the message loud and clear. Keep our names the fuck out of your mouth if you're not ready to handle the repercussions that came with talking like a bitch.

After that, shit calmed all the way down. There was no white flag of surrender or anything like that, they just left us the fuck alone from that point on.

Cognac and I finally got cool after some time. See, I don't respect suckers, and homie was far from a sucker. It was a mutual respect when it came to us. Even before we hung together, the respect was there, and it remained throughout.

I remember one day Cognac was beefing heavy with a dude named Lil' Mikey. I didn't have problems with homie, but if I'm with you and you got a problem with somebody, as long as I'm not like that with that person, then it's whatever. I stayed strapped and ready all the time.

We caught Lil' Mikey in the car with a chick, (I would later find out her name was Kayla) but we didn't give a fuck about her name. She could've been Oprah. Before I knew what was going on, big guns started coming from everywhere. Shit went crazy and dude was getting the business. Cognac said homie was trying to do him dirty, and we all know that if you beefing with anybody that's 'bout that shit, you better always have your guard up and your eyes open. I guess that nigga forgot to read the memo, because now it was all types of holes in his shit. I have to say Lil' Mikey was about that life. He ran into traffic and wrecked, but shorty was hit in the head. Shit got hot, and we got low.

Years later, Lil' Mikey got killed on some other shit. His murder is still unsolved. Cognac got charged with Attempted Murder for shooting Kayla in the head. He was the only one charged, and it was later dismissed due to lack of evidence.

Following that, I ran into this chick named Kayla. I got her number and talked to her on the phone a few times. I eventually convinced her to come chill with me. I took her to a cheap motel. We got to talking and it took her a while to loosen up, but when she did, she told me a story about how she got shot in the head. Shocked, I asked her by who? She told me that she was shot by Long, a dude from Haymount Hill, and Cognac from Nimmocks. My heart did somersaults and sweat drenched my body.

I scooted back and looked at her. So much time had passed, I was lost. *Could this be?* Hell no! She just said I shot her. She must have me fucked up; I didn't know who the fuck she was! Then it hit me... Wow! Small fucking world. This shit crazy. That's when I started connecting the dots.

Kayla…

My mind was reeling, going in all directions at once. The only way I saw to deal with that shit was straight up.

I looked her in her eyes, "Do you know who I am?" I asked in my most soothing voice.

She looked at me, kneading her hands together, "Of course, you're Larry boy."

"But do you really know who I am?" I asked again, needing her to understand the full scope of my question.

"No, I guess not," she said sweetly. "So, tell me then. Who are you?"

I took a long breath and let it out slow, "My name is Long, and I'm from Haymount Hill."

The look on her face was scary. I felt like I should've got the fuck out of that damn room A.S.A.P. But I couldn't, I had to get my name right with this girl.

"First off, you got it all wrong," I started. She was looking nervous. She'd scooted back away from me and appeared to be looking around for a way out, like I was about to kill her. I had to get right, get this shit under control.

"Before you panic, baby girl, I'm not on that type shit, I can call you a cab or take you home or whatever. Just let me know what you wanna do."

"You...you shot me," she whined.

"I didn't, is what I'm trying to tell you. That shit is street talk. Just give me a second to explain," I pleaded.

She did, and after it was over, she understood that I had nothing to do with that shit. The crazy part was, I still ended up getting the pussy. So, I guess it was safe to say, the truth truly can set you free.

Kayla, if you're reading this I wanna apologize for what you had to go through in your life, shorty. It's so many horrendous stories that float around about me, shorty, I'm used to it by now. I can't say I remember your sex game that night because it was a long time ago, and it was a one-time thing. Just know it wasn't you, shorty. You're awesome. It's just that in my line of work, I couldn't trust it. Sleeping with you is knowing the risk ain't worth the reward. That's the reason it was a one-time thing in that room.

CHAPTER 8
My Lil' Homies

For everybody that is reading this book and have never met me, or laid eyes on me, I want you to know, what you read is what you get. I am who I'm writing about. Some things have reached their peak and are slowly rolling back downhill. Some things will never roll back, so watch the shit you say or do to me because that same dude that I built from the ground up still remains. Don't ever get it twisted; I might laugh and joke these days. That's because I've learned how to keep the beast at bay. Not because I'm afraid of him, it's because I'm afraid of what he might do to everyone else. I've controlled him thus far, so I'm sure I can hold him down. The cage doesn't even have a door on it. He's being easy on my word alone. So, if it only takes a word to keep him in, you know it only takes a word to let him out. Back then though, it was hard to contain. I was continuously turnt all the way up.

I remember I used to run with my Lil Dunney's, B-Real, Lil Matrix, Lil Dontay, and Lil Metro. I had them niggas throwing rocks off the bridge when I was a lil' homie. See, they were from Savory Heights, and the thing about Savoy Heights is it's connected to Haymount Hill. It was basically the same place, but separated by name–and niggas, I might add, because they weren't Haymount Hill niggas. Far from us. There was a lot of soft dudes out there in the Heights. They got to the money though. I can give them that much. Gunplay or action of any kind was never their strong point, but getting money was. I'll never take that from them.

One thing about me that you need to know also is, I don't have a jealous bone in my body. I have nothing but respect for the niggas that came before me, that paved the way. The gangsters that came with me, I salute, even though we lost a lot of real ones along the way.

So yeah, I was fucking with a few dudes from Savoy Heights. Shit, it was impossible not to considering the proximity of our hoods. I used to fuck with Kato and Domo real heavy. Even got gangster with Roady after he did his bid (I think about 8 years.) That was my man. Now my Lil Dunney's were my heart though. They followed my lead from early on. These niggas ran where I ran. We were getting older now, so instead of throwing rocks off the bridge, we were throwing them in the streets. Get to it or get lost.

My man, Metro, was running his bag up. He was on his shit early. The same game I got from my OG's, I gave to them, and they soaked it up like they were supposed to. I paid a lot of attention to Metro, he was already a moldable nigga. I saw something in him. A light, maybe, I don't know. Something drew me to him. I built an early soft spot for this lil' nigga. Probably because he reminded me of me, and I knew how I gave it up, so I was sure he was solid too. A hundred. Savoy Heights had some real dudes coming out of there.

My lil' niggas was bout that life for real. There was a nigga named Red Boy that came out of there too. Now this nigga was one of the biggest hustlers that came out of Savoy Heights for real. He outshined his hood even. He was one of the biggest niggas that came out of the city. I'll give him that. He ran that shit for years. He went left instead of right when the FEDS stepped in though.

His right-hand man was this nigga named Yatta Man. These niggas were like Frick and Frack. Yatta Man put it down for Red Boy. He got that money for him. Yatta Man was a hustler and a rapper. Everybody knew this nigga. He was signed to Red's Boy's label, Triple 7. Yatta Man did a song with Gucci Mane called, "Re-Up" and "Aw-Man" off the *Trap-A-Thon* album when Gucci was signed to Big Cat Records. I don't know if he actually went in the studio and got it in person with Gucci, or added the track electronically, but that's none of my business. I'm telling my story.

This nigga Yatta Man was well known in the city. He might have busted his gun once or twice, I don't doubt that, but to me, in my eyes, homie wasn't 'bout that shit. (Yeah, I said that.)

Yatta Man had a little brother named, Da Da. Now this nigga Da Da was definitely on the money train. If you ask me, he was on the same level as Red Boy. So, it's safe to say that he was heavy. He also went left instead of right when the FEDS stepped in. Da Da fucked with this nigga named Doe Boy from St. Paul's. If you're from North Carolina, I'm almost positive you've heard of this nigga. His reach went way past the Carolinas, but his story is his story, and I'll let him tell that. I do know he went left instead of right when the FEDS stepped in. In the 'Ville money was plentiful and niggas was out this bitch getting it.

Since we're still talking about Savory Heights, I'll introduce y'all to C-Note. The "C" must have stood for Cotton, because this nigga was soft as hell. This nigga C-Note got his money from his mom who passed away and left him 6 figures or better. I'll give him credit though, he fucked all the bad bitches. He earned that much.

C-Note had a cousin named D-Ray that was my G. Now D-Ray was a hustler at the beginning; this nigga was buying bricks at an early age. C-Note used to try to boss up on the low. He used to try and manipulate our loyalty. He knew how loyal we were to D-Ray and he wanted that for himself. He would try to shine when bitches were around. I wasn't tripping on him too hard. I knew he was a sucker in boss clothing.

All that fake bossing came to a head when Kev robbed C-Note and Boo Shay, who is Kato's big brother. Man, Kev got his ass in his own house. He took everything in the house, and Boo Shay got it too, just for being there. Guilty by association. Back then, C-Note had a badass Acura Coupe on 20's. That shit was crazy back then! Kev took that shit too. This nigga was a baby Debo (LMFAO!!!)

I remember Kev calling me, asking where I was. I was on the Hill at the time, so I told him. When he pulled up, my eyes got big as hell. He was driving C-Note's Acura! I asked him where the fuck he got the car from. He told me to hop my ass in.

As soon as I got in, he told me that C-Note had tried to play him on some shit he just couldn't forgive or forget. We went to get a room to chill and chop it up, and when we got there Kev was smiling, and said it was on him. We called some bitches over so we could turn up with Kev's newly-acquired check. We got the hoes there and did what we do. Ain't no secret 'bout that.

A few hours later, Kev was taking back the hoes and I was chilling, waiting for him to get back. My phone rang and when I picked it up, I heard a nigga on the other end crying.

"Yo," I said, lying back on the bed like a boss. "What up?"

"Long man," the voice said in between tears. "Long, Kev robbed me, man. This C-Note, man."

I had to hold back my laughter. This nigga was actually crying like a bitch. It wasn't hard to believe; that's what bitches do, they cry.

"Calm down, bro," I said, still holding back laughter. "What's the problem?"

"Man, Lil Kev got me and Boo Shay. Why he do that to us, Long? I don't even care about that other shit. I just need my ring back. Please get the ring back for me, bro. It's the only thing I got to remind me of my mom's, yo," he pleaded.

"I got you, bro," I said seriously. "Let me holla at him."

As soon as I hung up the phone, Kev was coming through the door. He threw the keys down on the night stand and sat down.

"What's up?" Kev asked. "Why you looking crazy?"

"Man, Note just called me. He need that ring back. He was crying and shit. I had to get the fuck off the phone with homie," I explained.

Kev let time creep between us. I could see the stern look on his face. This nigga was crazy. It was all over his face. When he spoke, I knew it was final.

"Man, fuck him. I ain't giving that nigga shit! He better take heed from now on. You play games with kids." Shit, C-Note had a better chance at playing the lottery.

See, it's like this. Some dudes have heart and nuts, but no brains. They be shooting up club parking lots and doing stupid shit, hitting a bunch of innocent motherfuckers. Or robbing convenience stores, killing the clerk, catching fifty years, then get mad when their people don't send them money. Or they get mad at a nigga for fucking their bitch when she the one offered up the pussy. She ain't thinking 'bout you no more, you was a nobody from the jump. Be mad at yourself; you fucked up, you was playing out there in the motherfucking way.

Now, some dudes got brains but no nuts or heart. When they stack theirs up, it's easy for real niggas to take their shit and tell them, "get your soft ass out the streets!" Don't get it twisted; we don't hand pick our targets, looking for soft niggas. If they are about that shit like I am, they can get it too. I like them the best because they make me go harder. It brings out the best in me. The point I'm making is, dudes like me are rare. I come with nuts, heart, equipped with top-notch game, and I got brains.

Keep reading and you be the judge.

Lil' Kev (K. Cutta)

CHAPTER 9
My Weird Family

I read somewhere, '*Never let your fear decide your future.*' I swear I thought about that quote all day. Life is so funny. Sometimes you're up, sometimes you're down. The beauty of it all is, no matter what life throws our way, anything is better than death. As long as we're six feet above the ground, we can make a difference... only if we want to. See, that's the catch. We have to want to be something different. That want has to be so intense that it becomes a need, like air or water, life necessities. Without them, death is unavoidable. That's how much we have to look at what we risk in life.

Early on, I looked at life like living is whatever. I didn't see the beauty in it. Where I'm from, tomorrow isn't promised. Insurance policies should be a fucking mandate from birth, because a nigga didn't know if he'd live to see the next hour, fuck the next day. I can't lie, I was on the same shit. Really do or die, if it came my way. I'd start shit just to see if anybody wanted to take my place as a finisher. Now don't get it fucked up, a lot of the shit I got in was because niggas brought it on themselves. I've never respected suckers; I've told you that. So, if a sucker shining, I make sure to dim that light a little.

Looking back on my life now, writing about it, gives me a lot of time to reflect on how wild and crazy I was back then. It was tough back then. A lot of cold nights with everything I'm worth wrapped up in little plastic baggies, stuffed in my boxers. If you've never wondered where your next good-night sleep would come from, you don't even deserve the right to judge my life. If you've never been so hungry that you had a head splitting migraine for hours, I don't give a fuck about your non-struggling opinion, and I'm just being honest. I've never gave a damn what the next nigga did. That was his business. Only person I had full control over was me, Long, that's who. If I mix it up with you, then you were just in THE fucking way and you'll know better next time–if there's a next time. I'm not apologizing for shit. If anybody feeling some type of way, build a bridge and get over that shit because I promise you, I'm the last one you wanna bring that hot shit to. I don't do threats. For everybody that knows me, I do promise shit, and you can bet that shit.

So, know that I'm promising all of you that all this shit I'm saying in this book is how a nigga feels and really lived. I really don't give a damn if you like it or not. It's mine and I'm standing behind, on, and in, everything on these papers.

My bad, if I got a little long winded, I do that sometimes. I'm moving on though.

Death is crazy. It makes people pay more attention to their own mortality. They realize that we only get one life and the one we get isn't going to last forever. Of course, we'd love to live or have our loved one's live forever, but that shit just isn't so. We live, we laugh, we love, and then we die. It's the shit that we do in between that counts and pays homage to our legacies, like when my grandmother Ann died. This was my mother's mother. She died of AIDS, so if your ass is out there fucking raw, tighten up. That shit will kill your ass quicker than you think. I loved my grandmother and I miss her so much!

Y'all already know I couldn't go another chapter without introducing you to my family. One thing about these apples is, they didn't fall far from the tree because they got stuck in that bitch. (LMAO). If there was an award for the world's most dysfunctional family, mine would win consecutively, easily. I've never been delusional about how my family operates. It's off the chain. Shit, I got the T-Shirt, and wrote the book about it, pun definitely intended. With us, it was always somebody at somebody's throat. Somebody did somebody wrong and somebody was about to get hurt. That was the normal for us. If no one was beefing, then that was the time to get worried, because in my family somebody was beefing all the time. We didn't have a pause button, and if we did, it was broken way before I was born. Yet and still, I loved them and wouldn't trade them for the world. They were far from perfect, irrational, and turnt up most of the time, but they were mine and I'm willing to protect mine to the fullest. Wouldn't you? I can't say we got along all the time. Shit, I can't even say we got along most of the time because we didn't. We just tolerated each other until we could get the hell away from each other. Bottom line, we were and still are family. And that shit is until death do us the fuck part.

Where was I? Oh, I was talking about Koo-Koo's mother, my grandma Ann. The reason my family went more haywire than they already were is because without the glue, the house usually falls apart, and all they did. I didn't grow up in this household. I grew up on my dad's side, with my grandma May, but my grandma Ann lived on the same street–Clark Street–just a little way up the street. It was always a cousin, aunt, or uncle somewhere nearby, on either side.

My mother, Koo-Koo, was my grandma Ann's oldest daughter. She had four kids. Two were by my father, a boy–me, and a girl, Tomeka. She had one by Black Earl from the Hill, which is my little sister, Dreeka, and one by a guy named Boo Boo, which is my little brother, Boo. My Aunt Evon had two little boys, one by Fat Cat from the Murk (Murchison Road), and one by Ron from across the River. Kojack beat my Aunt Evon (which is his sister) in the head with a gun on the day my grandma was buried, but my Aunt Evon a "G" though. I ain't even gone get all the way into that story.

My Aunt Tammy had three kids. Two by a guy named Little Naji. (Little Naji also went left instead of right when the FEDS stepped in) and one by Jarvis. My Aunt Precious had two kids. One by a guy named Breece from the Heights. Now that's my man, he cool as shit. She also had a baby by Tarez, from down the way. Now he was soft as shit. He was Yatta Man do boy. My aunt Lil' Bit, who is my age, had a baby by the nigga Da Da. These were all of my grandma Ann's kids. (It's crazy how all her girls have babies by hustlers.)

Besides my aunts and my mother, there were also three boys: my three uncles, Kojack, Ant Lee, and Rick. Ant Lee is probably one of the smartest street dudes I've ever met, and I'm not saying that because he's my uncle. Facts are facts. He's been out the game for a while now. Ant Lee's probably around 45 years old now, and he only went to prison one time for six-to-eight months for popping Big D. This dude Ant Lee is a G, a real one. He's the kind of dude that if you get jazzy and pull your pistol on him, he's gonna call your bluff. He gonna make you use that shit or get the fuck on.

One time, Kojack had beef with a dude named Twan. They were at the Waffle House after the club. This nigga Twan pulled his pistol, and Ant Lee told him to do what the fuck he gotta do. Use the shit. He was ready to die. Well, Twan did just that. He used it. Only, he just used it on everybody else. This nigga ain't hit Ant Lee or Kojack. He hit innocent people. People in the Waffle House eating their food was hit. That shit was crazy. They gave Twan 80 years on state for that shit. I heard his homies did him in, but that's his story, so he gotta tell that.

My Uncle Rick... now this nigga was the quiet one. This nigga was slicker than a rain jacket. All the way out the way. Finally, there is Kojack. This dude is another story. Anywhere in any hood in my city, this nigga Kojack name rings bells. There is no way you can be from Fayetteville, North Carolina, and not know who the fuck my Uncle Kojack is.

I remember when I was 14, and I was riding with Kojack down the Murk. I was chilling on the passenger side smoking a blunt when a car came out of nowhere and cut us off. This nigga Kojack pulled up beside the car and unloaded his pistol into that bitch. Before I knew what was going on, we were on our way up the street like ain't shit happen. This nigga didn't even speed away. I would've thought we would be bending corners through the city trying to get back to where we roam. Instead, we were cruising along like we didn't just do a fucking drive by. (LMAO.)

When I got my shit together and finally looked at this nigga, I was tripping. This nigga was crazy. I got my shit together quick though. If he didn't give a fuck, I didn't either.

On another day, it was me and my smoker that owed me about $350. I'd been waiting on this little change for a minute, I wasn't about to let this dude out of my sight for nothing until I got my money. I asked my Uncle Kojack to use his rental car to go pick up my money this smoker owed me. He didn't hesitate, he threw me the keys and told me to go ahead and do what I had to do, but hurry back. The smoker and I jumped in and took off to the bank. When we got to the bank, ole' boy went in and got my money. When he came out and got in, I was ready to get back on my side. I wasn't even looking behind me. I wish I was because I ran right into this lady in a Town Car. I barely touched this bitch, but she immediately acted like she was T-boned. My heart almost jumped out of my chest. My dude that just paid me offered to switch places with me, but what the fuck would I look like to the police if they came up and I was in the car with this white dude looking like a straight hustler. Plus, we hit a white lady *and* I was dirty. I had a pistol and drugs on me. I didn't even let that thought take a seat in my mind. I jumped the fuck out and kept it pushing. As soon as I got in the clear, and had a chance to catch my breath, I called Kojack and told him what happened. I could feel the anger coming through the phone when he said,

"Man, don't you know I got all my fucking clothes in that car? I just got my shit out the cleaners! Long, I'm telling you, don't even come back to the Hill if you don't have my fucking clothes." Then he hung up.

Now knowing Kojack, I knew he had a lot of money in his gear, but what the fuck could I do about spilled milk. Nothing, not a damn thing. I mean, I'd be mad about my shit too. It had to be about twenty or thirty thousand worth of clothes in that car, so I knew this nigga was mad as hell. But what the fuck do I look like not going back to my hood because this nigga feeling some type of way. First of all, I'm a man. Second, this is where I'm from, so the only way I'm not going back to the Hill is if I'm locked up or dead. I was neither of those. So, I went and took it upon myself and got Ms. Helen to get me a rental car. After I got the car, I went right back to the Hill. It wasn't a nigga born that was 'bout to make me not go to my hood. If he was, I haven't met him yet.

As soon as I pulled in the hood I had my music playing. That Juvie was pouring out of the speakers. *'My people played me, but we ain't getting down no mo. That ain't how it supposed to be, but that's the way it's gone go.'*

Kojack was sitting on Ms. Baker porch. He saw me and I saw him. It was like a western showdown. He could hear what the speakers were giving to him loud and clear. I made sure I rewinded it at least three times before he raised off the porch. I didn't even wait, I just pulled off.

I did a little riding and thinking, then I went and picked up my little *dunnies,* Metro, and my other little homie. We were smoking and riding through the hood, slipping like a bitch. I'll never forget that white car blowing down on us from out of nowhere. I looked in the rear-view mirror and spotted Kojack. I could see something hanging out the window. I knew what it was as soon as I saw the flames, and felt the slugs hit the car. My lil' *dunnies* hit the deck, but I had to get the car under control, so I could send a few shots back. This nigga was crazy, it was on all the time with this fool. If it was war he wanted, then it was war on sight.

Two days later, it was Sunday, so "Sunday in the Park" was going on. Sunday in the Park was a day when all the hustlers and fly bitches met up off Robeson Street to chill and kick it. I knew this nigga would be out there. I had Jolina driving the same car this fool shot up. I was still mad as hell, so I put on a Jason mask and when I saw his ass, I unloaded the whole clip. I missed him though. After that, this nigga was waiting on me when I pulled up to my Grandma May house. He shot my shit up again, but he missed too. Before one of us killed the other, family intervened and, at least, got us to stop shooting at each other. Even still, I didn't talk to Kojack for a long time after that. Man, Unc, wild as shit yo. (LMAO)

Unc, you taught me so much, straight up. Our bond today has improved a whole lot. You remember you told me if anybody cross me, bust them, and that you were no exception. That's why I went at you the way you went at me. It's nothing personal; it's the game, right? Even though I was like 17 back then, I was ready for whatever, Unc, and if I ain't taking shit from you, I ain't taking shit from nobody. That's exactly how you taught me, right? So that means I was a great listener and student, Unc.

CHAPTER 10
Jack Boy Season

Damn, this shit is crazy. They say hindsight is 20/20. Looking back on all my bullshit, I'm sure that statement is true because I've been through some shit man. I've traveled some roads that most niggas wouldn't have dared to cross. I'm talking late night, when all the goons and goblins come out to suck the soul from the scared and innocent. See, I didn't just learn how to be around them, I became one of them. I learned all the tricks of the trade. I shut the fuck up and listened to all the teachings that the OG's saw fit to teach me. I watched, I reached, and I grabbed. I took the ball back down court so I could score.

See, now I was older, and I knew the tools that it took for me to make it in the game. Nothing was given freely. Everybody had to pay to play. There was no pity, no I-Owe-You's. The game was always what it was. It never changed, only the players. They got grimier and grimier every time a new breed jumped off the porch. They cursed earlier, fought earlier, shot guns earlier. Everything is being done a year or two before the generation that came before it.

It was crazy coming up in an era that held so much contempt for a weaker species. Suckers, clowns, anything or anybody that we deemed weak was fair game when it came to being the king of the proverbial jungle. Now don't get twisted, we went at *gun bussers* too because we was about that life. We will come see about you and see if you about that shit. I'm sure that a lot of victims that have crossed my path have said it wasn't fair. It's life! It isn't meant to be neither fair or unfair, it's meant to be just the fuck what it is–a journey.

Too many people focus on the destination, when they should be focusing on the journey, which is a thousand times more important than the destination. How we got there is way more important than getting there, because once you're there, if there were no lessons along the way, how soon we forgot about the whole trip.

Over the years, I've noticed that complacency is a number one reason we stay bogged down with bullshit over our lives. Trying to make the next person happy when we ourselves feel fucked up on the inside. Fuck that!! Nah, really, I mean that shit from the bottom of my heart. I did that once before, I'll never do it again. Ain't no way I'm about to make sure the next man is full when I'm starving. That's why I got on my jack-boy shit in the first place.

Oh, y'all remember that lil' nigga that used to cry when he heard his grandad talking about him? That same boy who used to whine when his cousins and aunts used to tell him that he needed to get out of his grandmother's house and go home, even when he didn't have a home to go to. The same boy that used to follow all the rules. (LOL.) Well, now he's older, tougher, wiser, stronger, and meaner. Plus, he's making his own set of rules, in his world, with a big ass gun that he don't mind using if those rules aren't followed to the letter.

Sometimes I wonder what would happen if the young Long ran into the Long I am today. I don't know. It's just a thought. I'm sure it would be an exciting conversation.

Did y'all hear me when I told y'all that I was truly a loose cannon back then? I was damn near a terrorist. All I was missing was a sorry-ass name like Saddam or Osama, and one of those long-ass shirt dresses them niggas be wearing in 200-degree weather.

I remember when I hit that nigga Da Da, Yatta Man's little brother. This nigga had birds like the fucking pet store. One day, I was chilling with my homie D-Ray at his house. We weren't doing much. I could tell he was waiting on something because of the way he was moving. I had no idea that he was waiting on this nigga Da Da until he pulled up. When he pulled up, he was with this nigga named Christ from New York.

When they came in they went directly to the kitchen like they were used to doing this shit. The kitchen was an open design, so I could hear everything that was going on. I heard them going back and forth about a price, but Da Da wasn't trying to hear none of that shit. He said he had to have all the change for what he'd came with. D-Ray said, "fuck it," he'd just take a brick-and-a-half. Da Da gave Christ the other half of joint and told him to go sit in the car while he counted the money. Christ bounced, and went outside.

I was definitely feeling some kind of way about them niggas trying to handle my dog about those prices. That shit was wack as hell to me. So, I went in and told D-Ray that I'd get with him later. They didn't really pay me any attention. I walked out the door and Christ was sitting in the car. I politely walked right up to the window and knocked on it a few times. He rolled it down and asked me what's up. I whipped the pistol out on his ass and told him to let me get that shit. His scary-ass kindly handed it over begging and pleading with me not to shoot. I told his ass to shut the fuck up, and he better not get out or try to follow me. I got in my car and pulled off with the half-brick sitting on the passenger seat looking like a fine ass white girl.

My phone rang about ten minutes later. D-Ray was on the phone. I already knew he was tight, so I let him say his spill.

"Long, what the fuck, man?" He said mad as hell. I saw smoke coming through the phone.

"D-Ray, I'm gonna tell you like this, man. Fuck them soft-ass niggas. They should've gave you that shit for what you had. They round here spittin' that big-money shit," I shot back, bending corners, trying to get to my destination. "If they weren't trying to make up for all that trickin', they would be okay right now. So, end of story, bro. Tell them clowns to charge it to the game."

The next day D-Ray was on my line again. As soon as I picked up he went to telling me about the conversation he had with Yatta Man. He told me that Yatta Man called and told him that I had to give that shit back. I thought that was funny. So, did D-Ray. He told me that he told that nigga Yatta Man they didn't want no smoke. They knew how I was giving it up. So, if they wanted it, they could get it. We hung up laughing at them clowns.

A little while later I pulled up in the Heights, and low and behold, all these same niggas were standing there kicking it. I pulled right up on their ass and hopped out.

They had to know I had that thing on me. Shit, that wasn't a secret and they knew I was ready to use it. I walked up and spoke directly to D-Ray, but I made eye contact with everyone of them suckers. D-Ray had this look on his face like he wanted to fall out laughing. He asked me what was up. I told him I was good, I was just making sure everything was all right. I then jumped in the truck I was driving and sped off.

A few days later, D-Ray and I were back on the phone again. He told me that Da Da said he wasn't worried about that shit. He said I'd be broke in a week. Little did they know, I was on my grind like never before. Shit, I was sending my money with D-Ray when he was copping from Yomi, this nigga from Rockingham. This nigga was building houses too. I blew down on these niggas and put my order in for a half-a-cake, but that shit never came. D-Ray said that he was trying to get at this nigga, but Yomi wasn't picking up.

They had me fucked all the way up if they thought I was about to go for some sucker shit like that. Hell No!!! Not Longhead.

If anybody thought they were going to play me like that, then they had another thing coming. Now we know D-Ray was (and still is) my man, but I was trying my hardest to wrap my head around how the fuck he got *his* shit while my shit was still in limbo. I felt like niggas were trying to play me.

I rolled up to D-Ray's studio, Block Burners. I hopped out the car with two Glocks on me fully loaded. D-Ray must have sensed that I was on some bullshit, because as soon as I walked in the door he said, "Long, you gonna shoot me now?"

D-Ray was a straight gangster, hands down. So, I knew homie was not scared. I just told him I needed my shit. That's when he told me that the nigga Yomi was mixing it up with Da Da and Christ. That's when I knew what I had to do.

I went and picked up my little Dunney's the next day and we went to Rockingham, about an hour away, fully strapped. We knew that something had to give. Either we were coming back with that work, in a body bag, or on a T.V. screen. Either way, shit was going to pop off.

As soon as soon as we pulled up to Yomi's spot he was sitting on the porch. He had to know what was up because he immediately said, "Damn, Long came to kill me."

I wasn't on joke time. This shit was straight kill mode. I told him that I came for my shit. Speed that because I needs that, and that was that on that. He had to know I meant business because he told me to hold on while he went in the house and got my shit…and he did.

I left that nigga without another word. He lucky I left him with his life for trying to play me. He had to know that I was ready to die for that shit.

I had another incident with this nigga named Jack from the Murk. Somebody broke in his house and hit his ass for about a *brick* and a lot of *bands*. Now I'll be honest, my little Dunney's tore his ass up, but their beef is my beef. So, when I heard that this nigga was running around talking crazy, I took it upon myself to address that shit. I went at his ass full-fledged.

At first, I couldn't find that nigga, and trust me, I was looking. So, to compensate for my efforts, I shut down all his money spots. I had to send the message that nobody was going to beef with Long and still make a dollar in the process. This nigga was good at hiding, but not forever though, because they say you find shit when you not looking for it.

I was in the mall minding my business when I ran into this clown. I was spending his money so I blew down on him knowing he wasn't really 'bout that shit. I walked up on him and looked at him like, *what's up?* He kept quiet, so I did what I did best–showed the fuck out.

I called the sales lady over and pulled out a knot of money. It was his money, and he saw it. I damn near screamed to the sales lady that I had a lot of money to spend. Instead of him saying something, this nigga just got low. Smart move, because he wasn't ready to die behind that shit, but I was.

Last but not least, this nigga Rolling Weight, soft as cotton. He was a rapper signed to Loud Mouth Records, owned by Doe Boy.

One day I'm sitting at D-Ray's house again (I know, don't judge me) when this nigga Rolling Weight pulls up to his house which is right beside D-Ray's new crib. My eyes got big as hell because I thought I stumbled upon a major lick! This nigga was a rapper, talking 'bout all this money shit. I knew I was about to come up.

I left D-Ray's house and went to get my man, Kato. We went right back over there and broke in this nigga's shit. When we got in there and hit the lick, we were sadly disappointed. This nigga had a few O's of crack, a half-pound of *Reggie* and a little ass .25 pistol. I swear, I wanted to smoke this fool for all that fronting and faking. I don't even know how this soft-ass nigga knew we did the move, but he found out and made a rap about that shit. Yep, a fucking rap. (LMFAO). He aired it on a radio station, Foxy 99.1, even though he didn't mention our names. It wasn't funny then though. That shit had me mad as hell.

So, one day Kato and I was at this lady Keyana Mama house and this nigga walked in looking stupid. We made it a point to holla at him outside. When we got outside, we asked him what was up with that shit he was talking about. Before he could answer with a weak-ass explanation, Kato slapped the shit out of his ass.

That nigga's girl went to taking up for his ass and told us to leave him alone. So, him and his girl was getting in the car, and before this nigga got in he turned around and yelled,

"I better not ever hear about this shit in the streets!"

I told him he wouldn't, and me and Kato rolled at this dude fronting like he was tough. He really was on some soft-ass shit and he didn't want no problems.

Da Da, if you reading this, tell the truth. Am I lying, homie? You know I speak the truth! Yo Jack, same goes for you. Am I lying? You know you didn't want no problems with me, and I was 17 going hard as a motherfucker. Yo, Rollin Weight, am I lying? Kato smacked you like a bitch! Didn't he? I don't care if you feel some type of way, just don't get in my way. I'm just telling the story how it happened.

Even though there were more robberies than this, I picked these three because these guys were very known in my city, so they stuck out.

CHAPTER 11
Dee Cobb

WOW! Love...

A great poet once said, *it's better to have loved once than to never have loved at all.*

Do you agree? I know I do. I believe in love, always have. The first female a man falls in love with is his mother. Well, in my case it was my grandmother. I love the ground this lady walks on, but that's a different kind of love. That's a timeless, endless love that has boundaries. Don't get me wrong, loving a girlfriend or wife, side bitch, or boo is heavy also, but is it timeless? Plus, it has boundaries. It's stipulated with what each partner can bring to the table, or how good they are in bed, or some simple made up reason we should love this person. So yeah, urban love has boundaries. And rules. I say *rules* because our other halves always set rules in place, and if we don't follow these rules they threaten to take their love away from us.

I don't do no faking. I've set my own rules in place more times than I want to remember. One thing I've learned over the years is when dealing with this superficial lust we mistake as love, it's never about what's now, it's always about what's coming next. You could go buy your lady a Benz 550 today, and tomorrow her homegirl could pull up in an Audi A8. Before the day is out, this bitch will be thinking about how to get an Audi A8. I've seen it a thousand times.

Don't get it fucked up though, some bitches deserve everything they got. Some bitches are just that official. It's some true to life, down ass bitches out there that really rock with their men through thick and thin. I am not talking about them. I am talking about those weak-ass bandwagon bitches that are only around when we're winning. As soon as shit looks like it's about to go South, they pack up with the rest of the birds and get the fuck out of dodge. The type of bitches that don't mind being called bitches in public because they know it's true. Shit, I can't lie; I've had my share. I've had more than my share actually, but that's how I learned that a real bad bitch isn't a bitch at all. A bad bitch is an intelligent woman with goals, morals, obtainable dreams, and ambition. The type of woman I'm almost positive my grandmother was when she was growing up. These types of women are rare, and they are worth all the time we put into them. These types of women don't come around but once in a lifetime, so my message to you, whoever is reading this... cherish her if she's a good one because they don't come a dime a dozen. It's a blessing to have been blessed with the opportunity to have known and rocked with a real woman.

I was blessed with a real woman at an early age, and her name was Deshandra Cobb.

Now, Dee is the epitome of what a ride-or-die chick supposed to be. I don't know how you rate yours, but if you've never slept in cars or abandoned houses, sold crack, or carried guns together, then your ryder is nothing like mine. I am who I am today because of this woman. For this, I pay homage to my homie, my lover, and my best friend.

Dee, I love you, girl! Know this!

Okay, so I'm sure you're probably wondering how I came to care about this lady like I do. Well, Ja Rule said it best: *Every thug needs a lady!*

I can remember it like it was yesterday. I met Dee at the barbershop in the city called, Bob's. She had on these red shorts that will be forever imprinted into my brain. She was with her friend, La'nadia. The crazy part about it is, La'nadia was the one I wanted first. I had my eyes set on her out the gate. I don't have a clue about how we would have turned out, or if we would've turned out any kind of way at all. No offense to La'nadia, but I wouldn't trade my time with Dee for nothing in the world. That's my dog, true shit!

I don't know if Dee wanted me then. I do know that I kinda sorta did some bullshit when we first started dealing to have her mad at me for a while. Well, at least when we were around people, she was mad. When we found some alone time, she loved on me the entire time.

Dee is an old breed of woman. She knows how to be in her man's corner. She knows how to make her man feel confident when he's not sure of himself. Dee motivated me back then as my first love, and she still motivates me today as my best friend. Bottom line, when you get me, you get Dee.

I remember Dee's Mom let me stay with them. I mean, I knew she was ok with me, but her motive behind that move was to use Dee's love for me to keep her only daughter in the house. She knew Dee would be there as long as I lived there. I would come to her window all times of night, and without any hesitation, she would come open the door for her boo. I swear I've been through some shit with Dee (LOL.)

I remember one day we were chilling in her room watching T.V. I was laid back like I was the king of the hill when Dee's uncle came in and told me that if I was going to stay there I needed to wash my damn feet. Apparently, they could smell my shit all the way through the house. I had no idea my shit was rocking like that! Shit, Dee didn't say a damn thing. That's when it hit me: either Dee had an iron nose, or this girl really did love me. For her to overlook the smell of my stinking feet, shorty had to be fucking with me hard body.

I look back on things like that now and I can't help but smile. This woman stayed up with me pulling all-nighters. We'd take a cat nap in whatever *beamer's* car we were driving for the night. She'd even serve the fiends when I was too tired to do it myself.

The Bible says, *love bears all things, believes all things, hopes all things, and endures all things.* It says, real love never fails. I am not talking about that play-play, just-because-we're-fucking love. I am talking about the kind of love that is a sacrifice within itself. I realized that no matter how much we try to even out the love in a relationship, we can't. One person is going to always love more than the other. It may be 55/45 or 80/20, but it's never 50/50. At least in my opinion.

We as men (myself included), in all our infamous ignorance, seem to always let at least seven good ones go before we realize the one we're currently with is a straight up *thotty*. By that time, when we wanna double back and catch one before they close the door completely, we're too late and they're on to the next.

That shit is crazy. I swear, I've made some crazy choices in my life, especially with Dee. This girl went to bat for me, even with her family. I was young, so I played a lot of mind games.

I remember Dee used to come looking for me, driving through the hood. She'd get out and look for my ass in hoodies, looking like nigga. This crazy girl used to have a big-ass knife ready to cut my ass or anybody that got in her way.

One time, I was at this chick house and Dee saw my ride. She came and banged on the doors and windows ready to fuck me up. I swear, I was in that bitch begging that girl not to open the door. I told her if she loved her life, then she'd be smart and stay inside with me.

Love makes you do crazy things, but it's great to have. If you have it, keep it. If you don't, find it. I think that's some sound advice coming from a nigga of my caliber.

To all of you ungrateful gold-digging sack-chasing thots out there that leave your man for dead when he can't provide like he used to, all I can say is *fuck you* from the bottom of my heart. It don't take much effort to be real. That shit comes naturally.

Dee, do you know my love for you has, and always will, stand the test of time. You deserve this chapter, and all the good things that life has in store for you. I salute you for being the '*BBIG',* 'Baddest Bitch in the Game.' There was so much I could have put in this chapter, like the time I chased you all over Fayetteville in my Benz and you were driving like a Nascar driver. I had to back off of you. (LOL.) Or the time you answered my phone and a girl was on it. You hit me in the eye with a pole and lumped my shit up. (LOL.) Remember the time you took my Benz and stayed out all night? You got home and I thought I killed you. I was all frantic, saying,

'Get up Dee, don't die on me!' You woke up and said, *'Boy I'm not dead...'* (LOL.) You're my forever and I'm your always, friends for life yo.

The song I always dedicated to Dee and she blushed when she heard it was Tupac's song, *Unconditional Love.* The second verse when Pac says, *'Just got the message, you been calling all week been out here hustling on theses streets, ain't had the chance to speak, but you know with you and me it's all 'g', we can never be enemies because you been such a good friend to me.'*

That's how I feel about Dee.

Dee, I can't say if your reading this because I know you are somewhere. During our 7 years of being together I wanna let you know... shorty, you were remarkable to me. Our friendship level has increased to it's fullest potential. You've been riding with me since my clumsy days, comfortable days, all the way to my cocky days. All I want you to know is, the reason we didn't work out was never you, it was always me. You are perfect, shorty, and I want you to know I love you forever and always!

Dee when I first met her.

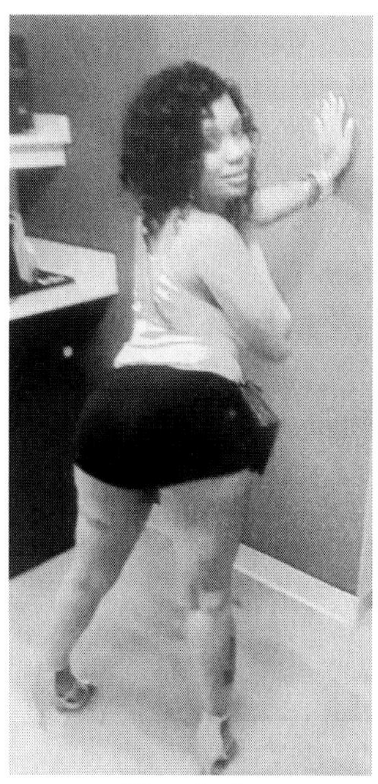

Dee today

CHAPTER 12
A Sad Day in the Hood

50 Cent once said, *'The good die young, but them grimey niggas live a long time.'* I don't think I truly understood the depth of these words until I had to face the reality of how fragile we are as humans. Our limited mortality is always a wake-up call. It's simple, we die—and we leave behind people that love us to pick up the pieces while continuously asking the infamous questions, *Why so soon? Why did God see fit to leave me here and take him/her?*

It's like a car that pulls up on a block. The guy comes out of the window and doors with rifles and pistols, and they start shooting shit up, everything that's moving, but they only came for one specific person. When the smoke clears, all types of people lay dead or injured on the sidewalk. An old lady, and a kid get smoked inside the houses. Shit is just crazy!

Hypothetically speaking, let's call him *Tommy*—Tommy is who the people in the cars are aiming for. Tommy was standing right where they could see him, and knock his head off, but when the smoke clears, Tommy is the only one that did not get hit. Everyone else paid for Tommy's grimey-ass ways. The next day, Tommy is right back being the dirty rotten nigga he has been his whole life while all the families of the innocent people who died are getting ready for funerals.

I learned a long time ago that we have to even out that scale in order to stay ahead of the game. Karma is a real bitch and in order to stay ahead you have to treat her like a real bitch. You have to tell her that she is beautiful, even when that bitch is looking like Medusa. You have to fuck her good on a regular basis, so she will stay in line with the rest of the bitches, destiny and fate. Ohhh, I've had a run in or two with Karma myself. I've also spent a lot of years ducking her get-back. I've seen how vicious and uncompromising she could be when it came time to return the favor. You will notice I say that life is short a lot—that's because it is, and we do not always see the ocean because we are paying too much attention to the beach.

Pain is temporary, it does not last forever. How we deal with the pain is what makes us unique. See me, I have always been the type to let my pain be my motivation. When shit get crazy, I get crazy right the fuck along with it. I'm not into holding anything back when it gets down to the get down for what is mine. I will climb the highest mountain on this earth to get my target. Everyone should know that by now!! Even though I have grown to have a mild tolerance for the weaker man – and that is only because there is more of them than there is of me – I still have a low tolerance for stupid shit. Nowadays, I try not to get close to people. Why? Because of the world that we live in. See, we do not live in corporate America where people work all of their lives to build up their 401K's so they can retire at sixty and die at seventy. Nah, we live where niggas stockpile ammo and guns so that they can live to see thirty.

I'm pretty sure you all have watched animal planet. That shit still fascinates the fuck out of me! That shit is worse than any hood in the world. I mean, it is a continuous hunt for me. I saw this pride of lions attack a heard of zebras. They damn near killed all the baby zebras while the parents watched. Helpless and hopeless. That made some wicked thoughts creep through my mind. I thought about what was I considered in my hood? I figure all I could be is a lion because I'm nowhere near a zebra. I'm the king of the jungle I live in—matter of fact, you could say I'm the real king of the hill.

I remember it like it was yesterday. I just made bond on a petty warrant. When I got to the hood I was walking down the street and saw a bunch of police. I was not thinking anything of it. When I got to the scene my heart dropped: they had yellow tape surrounding a lil' guy I learned to love. A lil' guy who every time he woke up he called me, and told me, "*Get up, we got to get this money.*" A lil' guy who used to tell me, "*I'm coming out of the house with no money today. Everything I made last night I put up like you taught me to*. A lil' guy who I used to run trains on all the hoes with. My lil' brother.

My fucking lil' brother Metro (Yep, you heard me right, Metro.) He was just laying there waiting on the ambulance. Then, he saw me and tried to get up. He stood on both of his feet and fell back down. I wanted so bad to go help my lil' homie but the police had this shit on lock. Everybody kept pulling me to the side, giving me the rundown on what happened. My emotions started to take over, and I walked back to the yellow tape—to look at my lil' homie, but the police had this shit on lock. At the time, I did not even know what was up. Everyone was yelling he only got hit in the leg. They thought he was going to be good. They were around him before the cops showed up.

The ambulance finally came to pick him up. I was filled with fury! All I could think was rage. I was telling myself, *It's time to go hard now. I still needed to talk to him 'cause I know there are two sides to every story.*

I wanted to tell him, *I taught you how to move, lil' homie. I always told you, don't get caught slippin'*. Little did I know that I would never see Metro again. I would never get the chance to talk to my lil' homie again. The last memory I have of him was him trying to stand. I was devastated.

Then I got a call from one of the big homies, Big Fred (from Haymount Hill.) He said, "What's up Long, what you got going on?"

I told him I was on the way to see Metro at the hospital. There was a silence then Big Fred finally said, "Long we can't go see Metro—Metro is no longer with us."

My heart broke into pieces. It was heartbreaking to hear those words. I shed real nigga tears! Right then and there, I broke the phone that delivered me the message. I love this lil' guy. He was my little protégé. I vowed to protect him at all cause because we were in this together. I lost a very valuable piece to my heart when Metro got killed. Lil' homie was only seventeen years old. My **WORD!** If he was here, he would be a hell of a nigga. He was young and swift.

I retreated into myself, and I cried for a thousand days, and a thousand nights. I was crushed! Ole' Longhead was not going for that; no way no how.

To make shit worse, when I went to see his mom, Ms. Sheila, she was crying in the living room. She burst out and said, "You were supposed to protect him! He was out there in them streets with you…"

I zoned out with nothing to say back. She was right, so right that the only thing I said before I left was, "I'm going to get those motherfuckers!"

The day of Metro's funeral, D-Ray pulled up pushing a new Mercedes-Benz. He had just took a loss with the white boy for sixty-grand, but I guess that did not hurt him. He hopped out with a Metro outfit. From head-to-toe on his jogging suit was pictures of my lil' homie.

D-Ray walked up on me and said, "Long, that was some fucked-up shit."

We went in and I saw my lil' brother in the casket. I don't know what I was feeling. I have to admit, I had some hard-mixed feelings. When I walked up to the casket I told my lil' homie, "I'm going to get those motherfuckers." Then I said my goodbyes and walked out.

After the funeral, one of my homies brought me a bag full of guns. This was to contribute to the war I was fixin' to start. I couldn't see any more of my lil' homies laying on their back, so I did not involve any of my other lil' homies, even though they were thirsty for blood.

I know people reading this are wondering: "Who killed Metro?" Well, this is what happened.

Yatta Man's house got broken into and they said that I did it. What puzzles me til this day is why did they not come after me? They knew I would feel the same way about my lil' homie. There was a kid named Cario from Haymount Hills—this dude just wanted some brownie points with Yatta Man. A kid named Debo from Savoy Heights—this nigga was Red Boy's ass kisser, and Cario was Yatta Man's ass kisser. To make a long story short, everyone said Yatta Man put a hit out on Metro. To tell you the truth, I find that hard to believe. I do feel that he was talking gangsta around his flunkies then they took it upon themselves to ride up on my lil' homie and shoot. Metro got hit with a Tec-9 (which was aimed at his leg); when it raised up, his leg and stomach suffered from the hit. That is what caused him to die from internal bleeding.

As luck had it, I never got the chance to catch Cario or Debo. Before you knew it, Debo and Cario were downtown on First-Degree Murder charges. From my understanding, Debo told someone he wasn't ready for any bodies, and he did not expect Cario to kill anybody. So, them being locked up only left Yatta Man. Now either this motherfucker Yatta Man walks around with a rabbit's foot or he has cat syndrome, because he has nine lives.

There have been multiple attempts on Yatta Man's life. One attempt was when he left a club on Nimmocks Avenue. Someone followed him and when he got on Robeson Street (right before you get under the bridge) they pulled up and unloaded those big boys inside. Yatta Man was not hit, but the passenger got lit the fuck up!

Another story I heard was someone waited outside of Big D's house off Ramsey Street where Yatta Man and Red Boy hung out and gambled on video games. When Yatta Man came outside, he was shot multiple times in the back (I think like six times. LOL.) Red Boy rushed him to the hospital where he, then again, survived. This is no LIE! I was thinking, what the fuck!?!?

Personally, I do not wish death on anyone; not even my enemies. IF you are asking for something, I will give you what you're asking for though. However you make it out, that's between you AND your God. Feel me?

Yatta Man saw me a few weeks after he got out of the hospital. He ran across me in Savoy Heights (next to his family's house.) Now, let me be the first to say: if I feel like you've been trying to kill me, no matter where I catch you at, it's on. When Yatta Man caught me, the only thing that separated us was a fence. It was our first conversation since Metro's death and all the shootings.

Yatta Man said, "Long, what's up?"

I got on defense mode. "What's up?" I asked aggressively.

Yatta Man said, "Long, I'm glad I caught you down here by my people's house, so I won't get kind of retarded. I keep hearing you shot me, Lil' Kev shot me, or Naji shot me. Then, you made a song called, *Do I Love My Kids*."

You wouldn't believe what this nigga did next. He raised up his shirt and showed me two brand new four-fives. Looking back, I should have took those shits from him, but there is a time and place for everything! Now was not the time.

I said, "That's what's up!"

Now, deep down inside Yatta Man only showed me those guns hoping it would stay in my mind that he stayed strapped. What Yatta Man didn't know was that shit DID not faze me at all.

I knew he busted a pistol or two; I've stated that already. Even if I'm beefing with a nigga, I'm not going to take anything from him that he deserves. So yeah, he shot a gun or two, but he knew deep down inside he was not ready for me and the shit I bring to the table.

After that, I really did not run into Yatta Man like that. I guess—only my guess now—he got low. A motherfucker was trying to kill him, and he knew it. He could talk till the clouds turn yellow. He knew he was a target.

Metro's death kind of reminded me of the Beanie Sigel song called, *Tales of a Hustler* when Omillio Sparks says, 'I find it difficult to talk to his mother.' I mean, what do you say to a woman that lost her only son to the game and a gun? I love that song, and to be honest, one night I had a dream that Metro walked up on me. The only thing he said was, "Who killed me?"

I told him flat out who killed him. He turned around and said, that's fucked up. Then he walked through the walls into the backyard. When I looked out the window I saw him going through the other yards. That was the last time I seen my lil' homie.

Cario ended up getting life in prison. He went to trial, I guess to see if his man Debo was going to take the stand—and he did. Sucka-ass motherfuckers! All I can say is, Cario, you safe at night. You got life, but you got your life."

As crazy as people are these days, do you think you would still be around if you were free? Those are only my assumptions, and assumptions can be deadly. LMAO!

Now at the same time I had all of this going on, I was having beef with a nigga named, Straw. Straw is originally from Haymount Hill. I told you, I do *not* jack anyone from my hood, and I mean that, but this dude Straw... he tried me on some sucka shit.

Straw had moved to the Murk (Murchison Road.) I knew where Straw and his girl were living at the time and his dope spot got broken into on the Murk. Now why would I go into his dope spot when I know where it's all at!? So, when I heard he put that on me, I told myself, if he wants it he can get it too. So, I brought him that real shit.

My homie Meat-Meat got hit and I made Straw stop serving and shut down all of his dope spots. Straw was hiding good though. There was even one story that they caught Straw in traffic in broad daylight on Pamalee Drive. He jumped out of his truck (in traffic) while it was still running to get away. He knew them boys was going to give it to him right then and there.

One day, I was riding through the Murk. I saw theses dudes from Preston Ave that hung with Straw. Even though they didn't have nothing to do with it, they got it too. No one is safe during war time. I hopped out in broad daylight and took their money, guns, and jewelry. Did I mention they were 8 deep? Later, them niggas showed up at Koo-Koo's house about 20-deep talking about I better be giving them they shit back, or there's going to be some problems. Even though me and Koo-Koo wasn't close, I wasn't going for that. Longhead ain't going for nothing, homie!

Allegedly, someone caught the two main dudes that was behind going to Koo Koo's house and chased them down. They unloaded into the car and his bitch ended up getting shot in the back. When she healed up and was released from the hospital, she made phone calls and told people to "let Long know she don't have anything to do with that. She's not with him anymore, ever since that night of the shooting."

I end up seeing those same two dudes in the club. I was by myself, yet they knew I had that flicker on me and was going to use it. In the end, they bought me drinks and wanted to squash the beef. They told me I could have that shit I took form them.

Now, to be honest, what I robbed them for was chicken feed. I had more than that. I took it cause I'm muthafuckin Longhead and it was war time.

I killed the beef and those niggas was happier then a faggot with a bag of dicks. They dick rode me every time they saw me in public.

Straw ended up killing the beef too. I liked ole' Straw; I didn't wanna do him dirty, but whether I like you or not, please don't make me act up. Straw knows I'm the real deal, as well as everyone else around this motherfucker. If it's on, I'm gonna come get you by my muthafuckin self too. I don't need no clique.

Mrs. Shela, if you're reading this, I want you to know I apologize to you and the Bradford family for going through this senseless tragedy. I want you to know I kept my word. I know this hurt you and Ashley, but no worries, I repped for the Lil homie. He didn't look up to me for nothing. That was my lil' brother. I love you and Ashley. Always and forever.

Rest in Peace, Delmetro Bradford. I love you, my nigga. Until we meet again.

(Lil Metro was gunned down on Ellis Street on Haymount Hill, right near where Chino was gunned down, right by Mr. Ed Baldwin's candy store.)

Yatta Man if you're reading this, you know me, homie. Even if you dislike what I am saying, you know

it's the truth and you can't do shit about it. I am him homie. Deep down inside, I scare you nigga. You know me personally. I'm not just about talk, there is action that back everything I've just said. Am I lying, nigga?

That's what I thought.

Slain teen remembered

No arrests made in shooting of 17-year-old

Delmetrol Bradford, 17, was shot and killed Saturday.

By Robert Boyer
Staff writer

Children gathered on the porch at 1013 Augusta Drive on Sunday to remember their friend, Delmetrol Bradford.

Inside, Bradford's relatives grieved and questioned why he died.

Fayetteville police said someone in a burgundy Ford F-150 pickup shot Bradford three or four times Saturday on Ellis Street, near Turnpike Road, just west of the Martin Luther King Jr. Freeway. Bradford was 17.

Sheila Shaw, Bradford's aunt, said police told the family that a man Bradford knew is a suspect.

Police would not say whether they have a suspect.

Bradford lived on Augusta Drive with Shaw and his cousin Ashley Shaw. The home, within a half mile of where Bradford was shot, is just north of Robeson Street.

Sheila Shaw said she raised Bradford since he was a week old. She said he had been suspended from Ramsey Street Alternative School but was trying to re-enroll.

Friends called Bradford "Metro," Shaw said.

Her nephew liked children and spent time with them at Myers Park Recreation Center, she said. He liked to play basketball and

See **DEATH**, Page 4B

Teen's killer given life without parole

A staff report

Nicario Levalle Christian was convicted of murder last week and sentenced to life in prison for the drive-by shooting death of 17-year-old Delmetrol Bradford.

Christian **Bradford**

A second man, Darius Vaness Evans, is on probation for his role in the December 2003 murder. He pleaded guilty in April to accessory after the fact and was sentenced Thursday after he testified last week against Christian, said Assistant District Attorney Cal Colyer.

Christian is 24 years old; Evans is 25.

Bradford, who lived at 1013 Augusta Drive, was shot on Ellis Street near Turnpike Road, west of the Martin Luther King Jr. Freeway, on Dec. 20, 2003.

Colyer said evidence showed ...at Evans was driving a pickup ...h Christian in the front pas... seat and two other men ...ck. When Christian saw ...rd, he drew a gun and ...im, hitting him twice.

One bullet went through Bradford's abdomen from the front, the other hit his right leg.

Evans drove the truck from the crime scene, Colyer said. He was originally charged with first-degree murder, but based on statements from him and the two men in the back of the truck, the charge was reduced to accessory after the fact.

Colyer said that Evans and the two passengers in the back all said that Christian was the shooter, as did two pedestrians who saw the shooting. The men in the truck said they were surprised when Christian brought out the gun and began shooting.

There were statements from witnesses that Christian had previously blamed Bradford for robbing his house and he was going to get back at him, Colyer said.

Christian's sentence is life without parole. Evans received a suspended sentence of 15 to 18 months, leaving him on probation for three years.

2nd man is charged

A staff report

A second man is charged in the killing of Delmetrol Bradford of Fayetteville.

Evans

Darius Vanness Evans, 24, of the 3100 block of Braddock Street, was charged Wednesday with first-degree murder and conspiracy.

Evans turned himself in to authorities about noon, a police report said. He is in the Cumberland County Jail without bail.

Fayetteville police say Evans and Nicario Levalle Christian of Fayetteville shot Bradford on Dec. 20 on Ellis Street.

Bradford was 17 and lived at 1013 Augusta Drive.

Christian is 23 and lives in the 1200 block of Branson Street. He turned himself in Wednesday and faces the same charges.

Bradford's family has said that he and Christian were friends.

Ellis Street

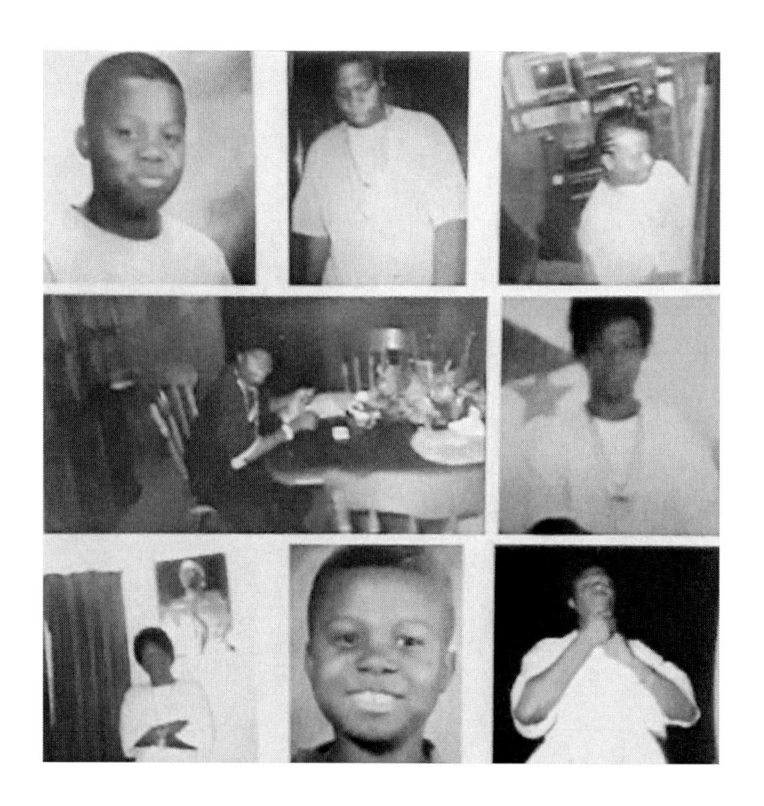

R.I.P. Lil' Metro

CHAPTER 13
Charges

Shit got hectic for me. I was still dealing with the death of my lil' partner, and still giving it to them bitch niggas around the city every chance I got. I took on so much beef at this time my plate was full.

Remember that same lil' nigga that went at his own Uncle Kojack? Well, imagine how I'm giving it to them, on sight, my nigga. My retaliation game had become so sophisticated, motherfuckers from everywhere were talking about how crazy Long from Haymount Hill was. There were stories on top of stories put on me. It was either, I shot somebody, or I robbed somebody. I was knee-deep in the streets at 18.

I remember one time I pulled up at my homie's house and three hoes were over there. I came in kicking it with my homie, making the girls laugh. (I forgot to tell you. I'm the life of the party; I'm going to make all the girls laugh.) So, I rolled a blunt and we were smoking. The shortest chick was hogging the blunt, so I said,

"Damn shorty, you tryna get higher then me. I'm Long from Haymount Hill."

Now, to be honest with you, reader, I was kinda joking but serious at the same time. All I know is that their eyes grew as big as dinner plates.

One of the girls said, "You Long from Haymount Hill?"

I said, "Yeah, why what's up?"

She replied to her friend, "Come on girl, let's get out of here!"

So, I said, "What happened, why y'all leaving?"

They replied, "Boy, you crazy! You ain't 'bout to kill us!"

These hoes got in their car and pulled off. It fucked me up. I promise, I can't make this shit up!

After they left, my homie said, "Damn, you genius, you done ran all the hoes away; pussy on you now."

I was still high, thinking like, *damn this what these people think of me? This is what this shit done came too?*

I snapped out of it and told my homie I ain't chasing no pussy, I'm chasing my enemies, fuck them hoes.

Around this time, I wasn't thinking about no bitches. I mean, I had Dee but shit, I didn't go there some nights. I was living in different crackhead houses. I wasn't worried about none of my hoes setting me up; they knew better. They would turn on you before me. Still, I knew I wasn't untouchable, that's why I always moved swiftly.

Now, to be honest with the reader, did I ever worry about a motherfucker hunting me down? Fuck no! If he was hunting me down, it was to tell me to relay a message to his mom what color outfit he wanted, and what kind of casket. I still moved slick, knowing that's just how I am. I use my head. I knew people were ducking me, trying not to get caught by me and the smoke I brought with me.

There was a lot going on in the city at this time. Remember that kid Doe Boy from St. Pauls, the one who I told you was winning around this time? Well, somebody kidnapped his 3-year-old daughter. Whoever did it was basically freed immediately, they were screaming my name before day break (I told you they blamed everything on me.)

Apparently, this is what I heard. This is how I got the story, just like everybody else heard it.

Someone snatched his daughter out his BM (baby mother) house late night. Then, they called Doe Boy and asked for 500 grand and 20 bricks. Now people, I'm no genius, but I know dope and money. That was a million dollars easily! Me, I'm not thinking nothing of this at the time. When I heard it, I was like damn! I even heard the kidnappers purchased the lil' girl McDonalds and fed her, so from my perspective they had no intentions of hurting that lil' girl. They just wanted Doe Boy to come off the money. This the story I heard like everybody else. So, when they flashed my picture on the news for that, I was like, *what the fuck? Y'all gonna blame everything on me*? *Damn, can I live?*

After seeing my picture on the news, I stayed low, ducking and dodging them people. I also was still finding time to give it to my enemies. I couldn't forget about them.

Then, before you know it, they were flashing my homie Meat-Meat picture on the news for the same shit. I was apprehended and stuck downtown on about a million-dollar bond. Now, like I've stated, I'm no rocket scientist; I knew there was no moving out of there. For now, I was stuck. I was still a teenager at this time and news traveled about me like never before. They did everything they could to damage my name.

They called me everything me but a child of GOD. Some were glad, most were scared, some were excited they could come out peaceful and run free. They knew where Long was, he was downtown on a big-boy bond that he couldn't make.

I was in a dark moment in my life, so I started doing some real soul searching to find myself. I had heart, nuts, and brains, but it was time to advance everything. I started studying books like the *48 Laws of Power, Get Anybody to do Anything,* and *The Art of Seduction.* Shit like that is how I advanced my skills.

See everybody ain't gone get everything. It's life. It's meant for some people to be dumb and it's meant for some people to be smart. The same with money, it's meant for some people to be rich and some poor. That's life.

Where was I... Oh yeah, in the county jail on a high bond, studying mind manipulation books.

Well you already know Mrs. May was riding with me heavy. She kept telling me she put this situation in GOD'S HANDs, and everything's gonna work out in my favor.

Guess who else was riding with a gangsta? Dee.

Now Dee was a ryder like I never seen. Believe it or not, Dee went and got a job. Every Friday when she got paid she would come visit me and show me her pay check stub. If she made $400, she would leave me $200. If she made $300 she would leave me $150. I had bands on my account for sho.

Hold up, let me stop the book for a second and tell Dee something... Damn Shorty, do they even get realer than you? You're a down-ass bitch for real for real!

Back to the story... While all this is going on, my big homie D-Ray is across the hall charged with First-degree murder. Now D-Ray was framed good, if you ask me. Remember when I told you D-Ray was buying bricks when he was young? Well, this is the story I got.

There was a white boy that knew somebody who had bricks (his people.) D-Ray got one from him and it was good. So, D-Ray and this other kid sent the white boy off with 60-grand to grab some more. The white boy—I think his name was Terry—was gone longer then expected. I think this Terry turned his phone off and was never heard from again. Now when you got a lil' homie like me, Terry who? I'm not even worth 60-grand at this time. You think I'm going to let somebody take something over here? Fuck no! D-Ray had a lot going on; he made the money back quick. So, the situation was that ain't nobody seen nor heard from Terry. So somewhere down the line, before D-Ray could get to Terry (if he was even looking for him because the last time I talked to D-Ray he said he was not thinking about the white boy) he came up missing. What D-Ray didn't know is that Terry went around and did this same act to numerous people. Well, somebody caught Terry off Old Raeford Road and unloaded them big boys inside. I'm talking a lot of shells! They ripped through Terry's car and he was shot in the head. Now they said Terry called D-Ray's name before he transitioned into the spirit world. They said D-Ray was the only one he could think of at that time.

Do I know if that's true? No. All I know is Terry was dead and about to be buried. Anybody could have caught Terry. He was into too much shit. I know D-Ray didn't have nothing to do with that nonsense. He had a bad bitch, was getting plenty money, and his record label, Block Burner was taking off.

Anyway, they charged D-Ray with that shit. He went to trial and they found him guilty and gave Big

Homie a Life sentence. I know I'm leaving out some valuable parts, but that's Big Homie's story so I'm gonna let him tell you that one. All I know is he across the hall from me and we stacked in this motherfucker.

I sat in the county jail for two years before they finally gave me a bond to the tune of 100 grand and I raised up out that motherfucker. Just like that, it was back to the streets I was missing, and time to pay a couple guys a visit for all the faking they were out there doing.

D-Ray, if you are reading this, homie... no matter how far I go in life, no matter how much money I touch, no matter how big I get. You gonna always be my big homie. I respect you as a man to the fullest. A go-getter. You already know what it is. When you hit my phone and ask for anything, it's done. Every time you ever called me and said send this money here, take this over here, it got done.

It will forever be like that until you raise up outta that motherfucker. I know you fighting for your appeal; keep fighting my nigga. Don't ever give up! Your innocence will show. I love you, my nigga. I know you hate when the FEDS picked me up because them other dudes don't keep it real like me. I know they out there lying to you. Not me though; wait till I touch. Haymount Hill in this motherfucker. I'm a real nigga for life!

‹an charged with 1st-degree murder

By Robert Boyer
Staff writer

Lawmen arrested a Fayetteville man Friday hours after a man he is accused of shooting died in the hospital.

Deray Yantell Jackson, 23, of the 1100 block of Wildwood Drive, is charged with first-degree murder and conspiracy. He is being held without bail.

Jackson is accused of shooting Terry Alan Guy in the head Monday on Old Raeford Road. Guy died Thursday night at Cape Fear Valley Medical Center.

Jackson | Guy

He was 23 and lived at 2688 George Owen Road.

Deputies and state probation and parole officers arrested Jackson outside his home about 1 a.m.

Sheriff's Maj. Sam Pennica said a dispute between Jackson and Guy over an October drug deal led to the shooting. Investigators think Jackson paid Guy for a "large quantity of marijuana," Pennica said.

Guy was a passenger in a Chevrolet Blazer that was stopped on Old Raeford Road at Raeford Road. Authorities say Jackson and at least one other man in a gold Chevrolet Trailblazer pulled alongside and began firing.

Pennica said lawmen are trying to identify the men in the Trailblazer.

Staff writer Robert Boyer can be reached at [illegible]

D-Ray shining

CHAPTER 14
Grandma I'm A Hustler

I'm back on the streets taking it light. I guess everybody was sitting around seeing what kinda move I'm gonna make. I could see the fear in their eyes when I pop up. Rumor around the city was that I had a big boy Hit on my head from Doe Boy. I wasn't worried about that too much. I was really ready to get back in grind mode and the swing of things. I wasn't even thinking about no pussy at this time. I went to the hood and got me a gun. That was my first move. When I got there everybody welcomed a gangsta back. I accepted the greetings while I observed everything, and you wouldn't believe who had the hood on lock. Remember my homie, Jig, who wasn't in the streets, my best friend? He had this shit on smash! He had a mean 20 flow. I sat in one of his fiends' houses one night and watched him clock about two-grand in *20* rocks that night. In my mind, I'm like, *this what's up!*

Jig gave me the rundown on what's been popping in the hood and the city. He broke me off some bread, gave me dap, and we split. I came back the next day and kicked it up there for the rest of the week. Every fiend that stopped by there knew me already, so they kept asking me when I was gonna be good. I told them this was brah shit, I was just chilling. Even though this was my best friend, I had to ask him just to make sure everything was cool. Although I knew he wouldn't mind, it was something *he* had built so I had to ask. So one night I asked Jig,

"Aye bruh, how would you feel if I got some work, sit in your spot, and take turns?"

Jig fired back, "Bruh, I can't believe you asked me no shit like that. You know damn well you can have half of what I got."

It reminded me of that 2pac song, *Until The End of Time.* When 'Pac says, '*In the hood true homies make you feel good.*'

I forgot to mention something earlier in the book. I got so caught up telling you these go-hard stories that I forgot to tell you I'm a hustler by nature. In the midst of doing all of those things you just read, I was still hustling and putting my money up also. Don't think we crash dummies or just jack boys. We do it all. Now, on a player slang, I'll tell you straight up, I play all positions in this baseball game. Back catcher, umpire, 1st base, 2nd base, 3rd base, outfield, dugout, the audience—I play it all. Simply put, what I'm saying is this: I like to get my work from the Mexicans, whip it, and front my work out (and you gonna pay me my money.) I'm going to be the one to pick it up. I'm going to be the one to knock a nigga down if he gets out of line.

In the process of me handling my business, I'm fucking all the bad bitches and never pillow talking. (Of course, I'm hitting them hoes with condoms.) I don't diss niggas in front of hoes for brownie points nor for pussy either. If I meet a chick and she is talking about her baby daddy or ex-boyfriend, saying he ain't shit... before she even finishes her statement I interrupt her (unlike I've seen so many other dudes do.)

Most niggas be on some simp shit, like, '*Oh, he's a lame. He did you like that?*" Meanwhile, he doesn't even know the guy. This guy could be a killer and he dissing him for some pussy. Me? I'll ask a hoe straight up when she finish bashing her ex: '*What did you do? You telling what he did.*' Or I'll tell a hoe: '*Sound like y'all in love. Y'all just having problems right now.*' Then they get mad because I'm a real nigga. I ain't feeding into that weak shit. Matter fact, if a girl give a dude some pussy after she see he weak minded for it, then she's a bum bitch herself and will let anybody crawl inside her hole. Over here homie, I ain't beefing about no bitch. That's number 1. I'm going to also take your shit if I feel you don't deserve it or if you are fronting. Plus, I'm going to respect all my elders and lookout for all the kids.

That's what I mean when I say, I play all positions of this baseball game. I'm not just talented in one position.

Now back to the story. I get carried away sometimes...

When Jig gave me his blessing to get money on his block, he even gave me some work. So, I started hustling out of his spot. What Jig didn't notice is I had money on my mind. I came out of jail on a mission. I was sharper than I'd ever been. I wasn't rushing to get it overnight though. I sat back and analyzed the flow of things.

One day, we were in Larry Bethune's house. Every time my man Larry hit that crack rock, he hunched the air like he had a piece of pussy in front of him (lol). I told Jig I was about to take this shit over. I started from the bottom, I didn't mind, I wasn't trippin'. I was out on bond, so I was chilling, just getting my money up. The

FEDS had just picked Doe Boy up. They knocked one of his tractor trailer trucks off with 190 bricks and 1.3 million dollars in cash or some shit like that. That's not my story though; it's his, so he gotta tell you the rest of it. So anyway, it was plentiful around the city for right now. It would soon dry up and I knew the time was now to get on.

Koo-Koo had a crackhead living with her in her shed. He was an old guy and his name was Mr. Tony. Because he was a retired veteran, he received 3,000 dollars every month.

One day I approached Mr. Tony. I sat with him and we had a talk. Turned out, he was a smart man. I'm telling you right now, just because someone smokes crack doesn't mean they're dumb. So, as we are kicking it, I asked him to loan me $1500 dollars on the 1st. I told him I would give it back by the 10th. I guess he could see the pain and anger in my eyes. I stressed the issue one time and sat back. As we were sitting in his shed, he changed the subject, but not before he told me he would run my request through Koo-Koo later that night to see what she says. Before I left, I ran it by Koo-Koo. I told her to let Mr. Tony know it was okay to loan me $1500. Koo-Koo from the streets; she game.

The next day when I saw Mr. Tony he told me to come back and see him on the 1st. Sure enough, on the 1st Mr. Tony put 1500 dollars in my hand and told me to do what I had to do. I looked him in his eyes and gave him my word.

I hit my cousin Footie up to get her baby daddy, Tom's number. That was my man, a hustling motherfucker. He turned me on to a kid named Seven out of the projects. (he went left instead of right when the

Feds stepped in. That's not my story though; that's his, he gotta tell you that one)

I purchased 2 ounces and a quarter, and I went hard, harder than ever. All I did was put everything up. Came out the house broke. Every day. By the 10th I paid Mr. Tony back and had about $3500 myself. After Mr. Tony saw the way I was going, he would pull up and kick it with me in the hood, knowing he was the reason for my come up. I would give him 8-balls and quarters on the house to go trick off.

Then, guess who I ran across? Da Da. Yep, you heard me right, Da Da.

I told Da Da straight up, "What's up, you need to serve me. I got my own money, I ain't on no bullshit."

Just like that, Da Da was serving me now. To me, Da Da was so happy I wasn't trying to rob him, he was giving me good deals. On the strength of that, I came up even harder. I was buying a half of brick before the month was out. Not only are we serving all the 20's in Jig's spot, but since my brother offered to split his 20 flow with me, I split my weight flow with him. Shit was rolling. In what seemed like overnight, we had all the niggas in the hood buying 8 balls and quarters from us. We needed a whip, but I wasn't about to start renting cars right now. I was stacking every dollar I could.

Mr. Tony came through in the clutch for me again. He let me get his car to make my moves in. I'll never forget, it was an old Saturn. That Saturn was my baby. (I ended up giving it to Terrell to get around in when he was on the run for a body.) I made more money out of the Saturn then a bank teller counted in a month. I took that Saturn and built a flow outside the hood also.

Jig didn't know half the people I knew in the streets. I could go on any side of town and serve. I wasn't worried about nobody doing shit to me. They were more worried about whether I was going to do something to them. People were happy to see me not on no bullshit. Didn't nobody want these problems! Hell, I didn't blame them.

You see, all the grimey niggas, jack boys, wolves, and vultures respect me. They knew I was the one leading the pack. Not only was I one of them, but I was hell on wheels and that's what they respected. I could do what the average nigga couldn't. Like the niggas who had work, they wouldn't venture to certain parts of town because they were afraid. I was fearless, so I could meet up and serve the jack boys late night when the average nigga wouldn't serve them at all. They loved to see a real nigga getting that money. They knew not to play with me at all. They could tell me a nigga just shot 10 people and robbed 5, and I'ma still serve you late night. I would walk in a house full of jack boys on *their* side of town late night like it was nothing. I didn't fear shit.

I met a nigga once and he said, "Long man, you one of the realest niggas to ever do this shit. Them other niggas ducking and hiding with the work. You'll come serve us in our hood, and all we do is rob. We respect you, homie. You a real motherfucker! We look up to you. We know you about that life *for real* for real."

Make a long story short, I combined my weight flow I built outside the hood with the weight flow I built in the hood with Jig. By this time, I was buying bricks. I went and got a black Benz and BMW. I didn't jack nobody either. I came up from $1,500 dollars. I told you, my hustle game like my respect game—turnt all the way the fuck up.

One day, I was down by Moore Street, and ran into Quan Murk. (My dad is supposed to be his brother Charles's dad. So, we're like brothers.) I asked him what he was up to. He told me he was buying a quarter, and I told him to hit me up. He hit me up for a quarter first, then he hit back so many times that next day after that, I knew he had a flow. So, I threw him some ounces. He started serving everybody down his way, and before you knew it Quan was buying bricks like me. All he needed was an opportunity. That's like my brother, so I loved the way he came up. I salute that shit to the fullest! Like me, he could serve jack boys too because they knew not to play with him. Quan done put certain shit down, but that's his story, I'll let him tell you that.

By now, I'm 22, riding luxury, and buying bricks. I got Dee stashed in some nice apartments decked out. Dee was cool to hold all the work, she wouldn't let nobody break in and take shit. She would tell you quick to get your soft ass outta there. I paved the way, it was me, Jig, and Quan's time. I was running down the same streets I paved. It couldn't get no better.

One day, I was coming through the hood in my Benz. On Branson Street, I spotted this fine light-skinned girl named, KeKe. I hopped out with the car parked in the middle of the road. She was pushing her brand-new baby.

She said, "Boy, you better get that car out the road."

I said, "Fuck that car, I see a walking angel. I had to see if you were real."

We went back to her aunt's house and talked. Turned out, her son's name was Travis, and her baby daddy was named Genesis. Now dude robbed everybody in the city, but guess who he knew not to play with? Me, that's who! I'll get to that later on though.

So, me and KeKe started kicking it and her son lil' Travis became my dog. She became my new boo. Keke was pretty as shit to me. Her voice used to make me melt. When I used to put this long crooked black dick in her she used to whisper, "Long, this is your pussy now. I'll do anything for you, where did you come from?"

What more could I ask for at this time? Young, balling, respected, and having the time of my life! This was too good to be true. Shit was about to go haywire again. I could just sense trouble. I'd been doing this too long. Too good to be true...

If you're reading this, and you still in the game, listen to the Big Homie. I done really live this shit, my nigga. When shit going too good, it's time to stop and observe everything. Something ain't right. Ain't nothing in life perfect. So, when shit look too perfect, my radar automatically goes up. I get on point. I like to say, shit get so sweet we start to relax. Hell, even sugar is sweet, but too much of it can give you diabetes. In this game, you can't slip. It'll cost you your life, homie. Whether it's prison or a casket, you don't get to choose, but you get one of them. Trust.

CHAPTER 15
My Mentor

I mean, where do I begin to tell you about Mo? See, Mo was a smoker. He smoked crack. I'll be the first to tell you, Mo wasn't a crack head, he just got high. There is a difference. The same way everyone who drinks alcohol is not an alcoholic, everyone who smokes crack is not a crackhead. I mean, Mo was not only my mentor, he was one of my great best friends. He taught me so much shit.

I used to go to Mo's house and talk for hours, just me and Mo. Mo is a different kind of dude. He used to tell me all the time,

"Aye Longhead, when it comes to this game, you a playing motherfucker. I ain't met no young nigga like you yet in my lifetime."

Mo gave me so much game. He brought a lot of things that was in my blind to the light. When I was young, I used to stash bricks in Mo's house. (I told you he smokes crack, right?)

To give you a better idea of who Mo was, this is the type of stuff he would teach me.

Mo would say, "Longhead, if you gone keep that shit here, you gotta put it up high. That means if the police hit or somebody break in, they gone miss it because they gone be looking down low."

So, we hid bricks in his vent in the ceiling. It was so smooth it didn't even look like it opened up. I would stay gone for days and Mo wouldn't touch a crumb. If he wanted something, he would go get something on credit. He knew when I popped back up, I'd pay his tab. He would be out the hole and smoke good. I gave Mo ounces like I gave niggas in the streets. Mo had more work than some dudes in the streets. He walked around with bands in his pocket. I felt more comfortable around Mo than anybody I knew. I knew he wouldn't bring me no harm. Mo one of the realest motherfuckers I ever met in my lifetime.

I would pull up at Mo's house some nights and he would be having a smokefest with other smokers. I would tell him I'd catch him later and leave. I could go to sleep comfortable, knowing they didn't know it was bricks in the ceiling, but Mo did.

I've been a lot of different places and met a lot of different people, but Mo was one of a kind. I shared secrets with Mo that I wouldn't tell no one else nor put in this book. That's how real Mo was. If Mo got locked up and I didn't know about it, I would find out when I went by his house and saw dishes in the sink and the bed not made. I would call the jail house, and there he would be waiting on me to find him. I would send my bondsman to get him out, leave him an 8-ball on the table, and lock the house back. (I'm the only one that ever had a key to Mo's house.)

When Mo got out, he would call me and say, "I knew when my nigga found out where I'm at he coming to get me."

Mo used to say he couldn't go wrong with me. I would respond that I can't go wrong with him. See, Mo knew a lot of my secrets, and he knew I had my bricks in his house. I could bank on him sitting downtown not saying shit though. You couldn't put a price on me and Mo's friendship. It was priceless.

I used to tell Mo, "I'm 'bout to tell you something, but you can't say nothing."

Mo would look me in my eyes and say, "We graveyard niggas, my nigga. You don't gotta say that. Everything we do or say around each other is going to the graveyard with us."

I used to laugh so hard. I knew he meant what he was saying. This was my nigga, man.

I remember one time Mo told me, "Longhead, I was way on the other side of town and heard a motherfucker talking about you. They said, 'that damn Long ain't meant to be played with.'"

Mo said he sat there quiet, but in his head he said, *you got that right, that's my nigga there.*

I burst out laughing! My mentor was giving my props.

It was a nigga named J-Dove, a money motherfucker. He was Red Boy's uncle. He used to go by Mo's house and kick it with him. He found out me and my team be over there and told Mo he wasn't coming over any more if we came by there. Mo said he told them that we were his niggas and that was his house. He didn't give a damn if he never came by that motherfucker again. He ended up leaving and not coming back.

When Mo told me that, I couldn't do nothing but respect him more. He was too real for this shit.

You know, my pops was never around, so the streets raised me. I learned the game, how to put certain shit down, from guys like Mo. I'm honored to have had those type of men to learn from. Mo, Kojack, and D-Ray.

I'm gonna give you some game that Mo gave me one time.

Mo told me, "Longhead, these hoes out here will play through their kids and tears. You know what I mean by play through their kids and tears?"

I said, "What you mean, Mo?"

Mo said, "What I mean is this: I was talking to this girl once. She had a daughter named Mia. Now to be honest, Longhead, I fell in love with her daughter more then I did this bitch. So, she had the nerve to call me and tell me all the time, 'Mia miss you; she been asking about you. She wanna see you.' Now, come on Longhead, Mia might like me—I'ma likable guy. But Mia ain't thinking about me. She thinking about cartoons and candy. *This bitch* miss me, trying to get me over there. So, she playing through her own kid to do so. Feel me?"

I nodded.

"What I mean by play through tears... they be crying a face full of tears, and if they get a sucker in front of them, he falling for that weak shit. All the while, she be laughing on the inside when it's working."

See, Mo taught me so much shit, a motherfucker wasn't ready for the shit I brought to the table. Nigga nor bitch, like Mo said, when it came to this game Longhead was a playing motherfucker. I can't relay everything Mo taught me; it would take the whole book. Be looking out for my other book coming called, *Do You Know the Person Beside You*, though. I share with you everything Mo taught me in there.

One day, when just me and him was sitting in his living room, Mo said, "Aye Long, let me borrow yo ear... In this world, you gotta be careful what you say," he schooled.

I said, "Why you say that, Mo?"

"When I was younger, Longhead, I used to say if I ever caught AIDS like these people, I'll just run in me a bank and go all out. Well I'm 53 years old, Long head, and I haven't ran in that bank yet."

See, what Mo was telling me was that he had caught AIDS. That made our bond tighter and made me not trust hoes even more. On my soul, my nigga, I never met anyone like Mo! Real to the core. Very trustworthy.

For example, if I brought someone over Mo's house and they were smoking a blunt, Mo wouldn't tell them he had Aids.

Instead, he would say, "Save me a piece of that blunt, player." Then they would offer him some. Mo would decline and say, "I don't let people smoke behind me, just save me the end of it."

I can't say it enough: that was my nigga!

Mo died of AIDS in 2015...
R.I.P. MO-LEE

Mo, I can't say enough with ink, to begin to explain what you meant to me, and how I feel about you. I watched you and my grandmother Ann die of AIDS. That's why I wear condoms now. I knew it was real.

Mo, I know you used to say, when it comes to this game I was a playing motherfucker, and I taught you as much as you taught me. Mo, I just wanna say you introduced me to the true meaning of real friendship. I know I didn't make it to your funeral due to my incarceration, but Kojack said he went to show our love and support.

Aye Mo, if you can hear me... from the bottom of my heart, you one of the realest guys I ever met in my life. You always said we was graveyard niggas. I promise you, you took some of my most best-kept secrets with you. I love you, my nigga! R.I.P. until we meet again.

There won't be another Mo in my lifetime.

In Loving Memory
Of
Mr. Moses Lee McNeill

Sunrise
January 7, 1959

Sunset
June 27, 2015

Friday, July 3, 2015
1:00 O'clock in the Afternoon
Faith Family Worship Center
137 Meadowcroft Drive
Fayetteville, North Carolina
Pastor Richard Pia, Officiating

CHAPTER 16
Game Changer

How could I ever forget this moment? How could I ever erase this tragedy from my brain? Seeing her face with tears rolling down her cheeks as she was on the phone with 911…

I remember it like it was yesterday. It was a warm day in December. Christmas was like a week away and everything was going perfect. I'm out on bond, buying bricks, moving them shits in and out. Everything's sweet.

I was in my grandmother's house on Clark Street, Haymount Hill bound. I was speaking to my Aunt Teen and my cousin, Welt (Footie's sister.) Grandma was running back and forth to the kitchen cooking a nice meal. So, as I wrapped it up I told them I'd be back. Grandma said what she always said as I walked out, *Be careful, son.*

I walked up the street to the girl's house, still on the same block. So, me and the girl in there kicking the shit. I'm trying to convince her to give me some head while her boyfriend gone. I wanted her to swallow it then kiss him when he walked back in the door. So, she game. (I guess the thought of it made her wet.) Before we could get in the groove of things and she could suck this long crooked black dick and do what we agreed to do, two loud gunshots rang out.

Boom! Boom!

This the hood. I hear gunshots all the time, so I didn't even flinch. It's normal. Hell, I think I barely peeked out the window. I didn't see nothing, so I kept on my mission for this head, until her son came in the house out of breath.

He had just saw me come to his house, so he knew I was there. I'll never forget the message that lil' guy delivered.

Gasping for breath, he said, "Long, somebody just shot up your grandma house!"

I looked at that lil' boy like he was a grown man and said, "Little boy, I don't play games; find you somebody to play with."

He insisted, "I'm for real, Long! Come look."

When he said that, I knew this lil' boy was telling the truth. I was out of that house in a flash and up the street. I got to my grandma's house in 2.1 seconds.

When I arrived at the front door, I saw the bullet holes and the shattered glass. I paused for a second. I was nervous than a motherfucker! As I froze in shock, I recalled something when I was a little boy in that same living room.

Grandma told me a story about an incident that happened before I was born. This old man shot up her house with my aunts and uncle in it. My grandad came from the neighbor's house and shot the man. My aunts and uncles were just kids at the time. Like them, I was still a kid when my grandma told me the story, so I asked her a question like a kid would. I asked her, did he die? Grandma never told me he died, she just said they sure buried him. (LMAO my grandma got a way with words.)

I'll be a lie and the truth ain't in me if I tell you I was angry. I was scared, scared to see what was on the other side of the door. When I opened the screen door, glass fell everywhere. I walked in and my Aunt Teen immediately said,

"Why are you shooting in this house, boy? What's wrong with you?"

My cousin Welt was still in shock mode with her eyes wide, while my Aunt Teen just cried. (Now mind you, nobody on this side of my family are in the streets except me.)

I ignored her question and took off through the house. I was searching for that sweet woman that used to tell me that nobody had to love me because her and GOD loved me.

When I rushed into the kitchen, there she was... my 72 ½ year-old precious grandma kneeling beside the refrigerator, crying on the phone with 911. When I first saw the woman my world revolved around kneeling on the floor crying, I can't explain to you even to this day how it made me feel.

When I approached her, I looked her in her crying eyes and whispered, "Are you ok?"

She nodded her head while still on the phone with 911. I made sure she was ok, then told her I was going outside. When I turned to walk out the door, she grabbed my coat. I knew she was worried about me, so I turned around to confirm to her that I was going on the porch. To be honest, that was over 10 years ago, and I still feel the same emotions writing this to you right now.

As I walked past my aunt and cousin, I told them everything was going to be ok. Then I walked outside to find a cigarette. I needed to smoke something right then because my nerves were bad.

While I was outside blowing out smoke, all I could picture was my grandma's pretty, sweet face. A woman that protected me, prayed for me, and loved me when nobody else wouldn't. I was trying to wrap my mind on who had the elephant nuts to try and hurt my 72-year-old grandmother. When I was in the streets, I never touched anybody's elderly parents. Now I would be a lie if I told you I didn't want revenge. Little did I know, I wouldn't be able to get it.

Am I sad I didn't get my revenge? Fuck yeah! I wanted to punish the man who did this. The only problem was, I didn't know who did it. However, I came to know who did it after the fact. This is the story I heard, after reading *Motions*, and stories in the streets.

They say a guy named Buck from Massey Hill and some other guy I didn't even know shot up my grandma's house. They say it was behind another family member. That was puzzling to me because none of my family over there was in the streets. Well anyway, the way I heard it was that Buck and his homie named Bobby did the shooting. Buck and Bobby shot up my grandma's house and shot at some more people that day. They went on a robbing spree and robbed a bunch of people. These lil' niggas must have been on dope, some strong shit. So, after they left Haymount Hill, they went and did some more shit to somebody else. They was cutting the fuck up. I heard all these stories afterwards, but this is where I come in at.

After my grandma's house got shot up, about an hour later somebody caught them boys downtown on the city streets in broad daylight and put 60 to 70 holes in their car at a stoplight with all kinds of traffic around. They fucked up down the line with some serious people. The boy Buck must have 9 lives because he got hit but survived. From my understanding, he drove his homie to High Smith Rainey Hospital, kicked him out at the front door, and pulled off. He died right after that. They tell me this how they said I went from finding a cigarette to smoke, to finding somebody I didn't even know.

I didn't know who shot my grandma's house up until later. So, after the homicide detectives found the car with all the holes in it, and caught up with Buck, he told them I killed his homie.

Now let me tell you something and it goes like this: I guess the police determined they shot up my grandma's house. I don't know if Buck told them that or they matched the shells in his car with the shells from my grandma's house. Like I told you, I didn't know any of this. I found all this out later. I was lost at first.

Back to what I'm saying though... How this lil' nigga gonna say he saw me shooting into his car? We street niggas! If somebody putting 60 to 70 holes in your car, do you think you gonna look and see who shooting? Fuck no! Not even me. I'm getting low, hoping for survival and praying retaliation.

Bobby was dead and about to be buried. Now when his kids grow up and ask did they daddy get killed, their people can say, they sure buried him. (LMAO). If you asking me as a man, do I have remorse for Bobby and his family, I'll tell you the truth: Fuck no I don't got no sympathy for him nor his family. Where is he buried at so I can go piss on his grave? Whoever they crossed didn't play either. I guess that's fair to say because they got him and his homie good. Real street shit, I don't give a fuck about Bobby after his lying ass homie Buck told the police it was me and my people Quan Murk. I felt he only lied because he knew what he had done, and he know how I'm coming. The only thing was, I didn't know what he had done.

So, right before Christmas in 2007, me and Quan was on the TV screen for First Degree Murder. So, here I go again, back on the news for something I hadn't done. I knew shit was going too sweet. I'd just gotten out of the County Jail, and I was still out on bond too. This shit was wild dog…

I know my grandmother won't ever read this book. She is a Christian lady, a God-fearing woman, but I want the readers to know I'll kill a brick and put a rock in the hospital for this woman. In life, if you have nothing you will kill or die for, you're not fit to live. Just know if I could read your mind, and you even thought of doing something to this sweet, precious woman—just a thought—I'll blow your brains out in front of the police, turn myself in, and go to sleep happy at night. Bet your last dollar on that and watch it double to two.

Just to make it clearer from my perspective... remember that lil' boy that used to cry his heart out because he felt no one loved him and this sweet woman used to comfort him and protect him by all means? How far do you think this guy you're reading about now will go for her?

I'm done talking about it. Next chapter...

1 Charged, 3 Sought in Fayetteville Slaying

Posted December 28, 2007

FAYETTEVILLE, N.C. — Police were searching Friday for three men in connection with the shooting death of a Fayetteville man a week ago.

Bobby Eugene Clemmons, 23, was left at the emergency entrance to Highsmith Rainey Hospital on Dec. 19 after being shot, and he later died, police said.

Police recovered the vehicle they believe Clemmons was in when he was dropped off at the hospital. The black Kia was located near Fordham Drive.

The location where the shooting occurred hasn't yet been determined, police said.

David William Covington, 23, of 204 Brinkley St., was arrested Thursday and charged with first-degree murder, attempted first-degree murder, assault with a deadly weapon with intent to kill, conspiracy to commit murder and shooting into an occupied vehicle. He was being held in the Cumberland County Detention Center on a $210,000 secured bond.

Police were searching for the following men in the case:

Larry Donnell Everett, 23, of 1110 Clark St.; Kajuan Kenneth Toles, 24, of 827-A Orange St.; and Ricky Lavelle Martin Jr., 19, of 289 Ingram St.

Another man who was identified last week as a person of interest in the case has been questioned and released, police said.

Anyone with information about their whereabouts is asked to call the Fayetteville Police Department at 910-433-1856 or Crime Stoppers at 910-483-8477.

Grandma House

CHAPTER 17
On The Run

So, it went like this... here I am on the news for First-Degree murder. Me and Quan spoke and we knew we hadn't done shit, so he said he was turning himself in. I told him I was coming right behind him.

When Quan went down there, and they didn't give him a bond, I was like, *fuck that!* I'm not going down there. I just got out the county jail after being down 2 years. I was already out on bond. So, I got low super low.

Now Dee was still my ryder, but everybody knew I fucked with her, so I fell back from Dee. I knew she would be there for me if I needed her though.

Remember that chick KeKe I met on Haymount Hill? She was loving me at this time. Her mom, Mrs. Evette, was loving me too. So, they hid me out really good. Mrs. Evette stopped company from coming to her house just for me. Man, them some real people. KeKe was sad that I was on the run, but she loved seeing me all the time.

I couldn't stay in one spot too long, so Koo-Koo stashed me at her spot for a lil' while until I was ready to go. I had multiple pads to go to. I was moving around the city like I wasn't on the run.

I had a friend named Tiffany. Now this chick was my dog. Tiffany turned me on to fuck all her homegirls. They let me live in their houses and knew I was fucking all of them. I was even fucking Tiffany too. There were times that it would be me, Tiffany, and her homegirls, and I was literally fucking every girl in the house. They were cooking for me, making moves for me, and everything. It was crazy. If you ask me, I don't know if they were giving me sympathy pussy or they just heard so much about a nigga they wanted to fuck a gangsta before the police got him. Who knows? It worked in my favor though.

Man, around this time everybody opened the door for me. People knew I was a good nigga, I just went hard in the streets. I'm gonna make all the girls laugh and be the life of the party. I had so many hoes with their back doors unlocked you never knew when I was coming. Jig, my homie, let me come stay with him and his bitch, MeMe on Ramsey Street. I was fucking MeMe's road dawg, Renee. This bitch was crazy! She liked to play with them guns, my type of bitch. When I say all the hoes knew I was on the run but gave me all the pussy and did everything I asked, I can't express it enough. Tiffany used to say to me, *'you a hoe, but you a clean hoe. You ain't fucking nobody raw.'*

One day, MeMe told me she had a friend at work named, Shay. She said she told her all about me and she wanted to meet me. She said she told her I couldn't be around people and that she was cool with that. I met Shay and she turned out to be one of my thoroughest ryders. She gave me her car, rented cars for me, and all. Here I am on the run and she is going hard for me.

Shay was off the record, nobody knew about her, except MeMe. I wasn't worried about MeMe saying shit, although MeMe did get mad at me one time. Her 18-year-old sister came down from Charlotte, North Carolina and MeMe told me I better not fuck her sister because I had too many hoes. Well, late night, on the run for murder, and a thick young bitch in front of you, what would you do? I went for what I know! I grabbed the condom and talked her out that pussy. She kept saying MeMe told her she better not fuck me. I told her fuck MeMe, then I got her wet and dragged that pussy in MeMe's living room. I'll talk a fish out his fin and sell it back to him.

Now, I forgot to tell you that my dick game is serious. She kept saying she never had no dick this serious. I put that thug passion on her ass like I did all the hoes.

Guess what? This young bitch woke up the next morning and told MeMe we fucked. (I ain't no genius, but I could have sworn I told this bitch not to tell anybody. How can I blame her though? They say my dick game is serious.) MeMe was super hot with me. She knew I didn't give a fuck about her sister.

The bitch Shay that MeMe put me down with was the truth. Her head was so good I told her to let me cut it off and take it with me. She was a professional at sucking dick! Where is she at now? Damn.

During this time, don't think my street sense fell off. Money was still priority #1. It was just a different format; now I had the hoes going to serve. I had to keep the flow going. I was still copping and cooking at the hoes' houses.

Even though I distanced myself from Dee, I would still hit her. Dee had two friends named Lanadia and Keshawna. Lanadia was Quan's boo. These two girls broke their necks for me. They would come get me, no matter where I was or the time of the night. My motherfucking dawgs, nobody cared about hiding me out.

I stayed free for a while, running around the city, until one day I was at KeKe's mama house. Keke had just left to go to her apartment in Grove View Terrace, the projects. So, when she didn't come back on time, I called her. She didn't pick up, so I called back again. Shit, me and lil' Travis was hungry. She finally picked up and I heard her arguing with somebody.

I said, "KeKe who are you arguing with?"

"I'm arguing with the police," she said. "It's a million of them out here at my house looking for a boy named Long. I told them I don't know no damn Long! It's U.S. Marshals out here also; they are getting a key to go in my house because I told them I don't have a key. They keep asking why I'm hiding out a kidnapper and a murderer."

I said, "KeKe, handle your business, shorty. It sounds like you busy, and don't come straight back here when you leave there."

She said, "Oh I know, I'm not slow."

Let me stop the book for a second... KeKe, damn shorty, you a ryder, and your mom's a "G" too. GOD blessed me with some ryders.

Shit was getting too hot for me in the city. The U.S. Marshals had my case. I was considered Fayetteville's Most Wanted Violent Fugitive. I knew it was time to scat. Honestly, if they don't know where you are, how they gonna find you? I had some people that was willing to hide me out until the end of time. The risk wasn't worth the reward. They turned the pressure up looking for me. I had hoes trying to give me enough pussy to last me a lifetime, niggas scared, some happy, and most real niggas pissed. I had police doing all they could to get me off the streets. I wasn't going. I'm way too brilliant, I had to pull out some of my mind manipulation at its finest. That's exactly what I did.

I had one of my bitches rent me a car and I linked up with the kid Domo from Savoy Heights. He had just come home from a 5-year stretch. They say he killed somebody, but he didn't. They couldn't prove murder, so they dropped it to Manslaughter. Well anyway, Domo came along and drove me out of town. Me and Domo knew each other really well. Dude a gangsta and 3500. He told me, "If you on the run, then I'm on the run." He put his life on hold for me when his name was clear.

I used to tell Domo, "Brah, ain't no use in speeding while you driving, always make sure our seat belts on, and no loud music."

That advice alone kept us safe for a long time, for all of you who don't know how to hustle from behind the wheel.

To be honest, we had no real destination. I just hopped in the car with Domo and hit another city. We headed to a city called Greensboro, North Carolina. I had a cousin named Shameda that lived up there. She is my Aunt Ann's daughter. It took us an hour and a half to get there. We pulled up on High Point Road and felt relief. It was relaxing to be in a new environment and out of Fayetteville, North Carolina. We immediately looked for a hotel. The first nice hotel I spotted, I told Domo to pull up right there. It was the Kourey Convention Center, 5-Star Hotel on High Point Road, just in front of the mall. Now, when you on the run for Murder, you can't be living in no rinky-dink hotels. They be having shit going on, the police could pull up and knock you off on some humbug shit. I'll teach you about that in, *Do You Know the Person Beside You.*

The rooms were $250 a night with a $250 deposit because we lacked a credit card. Dom went in and booked it for a couple nights. Shit, we were ready to rest good in that motherfucker. They put us on a high floor, and I stared out the window at this new city I just entered. Right then, I put Fayetteville in my rear-view mirror. It reminded me of the movie, *Heat,* when DeNiro said never get too attached to something you can't leave in 30 seconds flat when you feel the heat around the corner. That was us, feeling the heat around the corner so we bailed.

Me and Domo was just sitting around the room chilling. For all you slow motherfuckers, if I'm telling you I am paying $250 a night for a room, that means I'm still holding. I still got niggas pumping my work in the city. I got my nigga Mo serving for me, making sure all the money right. I still got work in his ceiling too at this time. I was just on the run and couldn't be seen.

So, Wednesday came around. I told Domo we had to go out, I gotta meet a bitch so we can get us a low-key spot. He agreed.

Now my new mission was to meet a bitch and hit her with this dope dick. She gets addicted, then I run the show. Well, we were about to see if my calculations were right or not.

If you ever been in Greensboro, you know our hotel is right in the same parking lot as the mall. Me and Domo walked over there and got fresh to death (we tryna catch fresh fish) for the club that was popping the next night. It was called *Ménage,* off Highpoint Road. Back then, I told Dom before we went out on our mission, if he meets a clique before me, bring them to me. This was not to say Dom didn't have no game, I was just the life of the party. I been around so many girls, I knew them like the back of my hand. I know how to go in and manipulate so fast their heads will spin. Straight attack mode! Once she smiled at my style, you won't see her for a while.

So, on Thursday night, we went to Ménage. Domo got straight in. I got hassled so I had to pay extra for not having I.D. Man, I'm 23 years old, on the run. What I need with an I.D.?

Once we got in, we went straight to the bar. I felt we could get pissy drunk since our big hotel was literally two seconds from the club, walking distance. We were tossing them shots back and I start to feel the liquor. I ran across two chicks, Aqueena and Ashley. I asked them what was up and we started talking. I asked them where were their other homegirls. If they didn't have any homies with them, I had to have them. If they did, we wanted all of them in front of us so we could pick and choose who we wanted (oooh girl, they are choosing. LOL.)

So, they went and got Janay and this other light-skinned girl who name I forgot. When I saw Janay back then, I knew I had my target. She was petite and light brown with nice, long natural hair. I immediately started purchasing them drinks. I knew our mission. We needed a place to live. I'm from Haymount Hill; I grew up on manipulating hoes. Clark Street motherfucker.

They were hanging around laughing and getting drunk. I pulled Dom to the side and told him it's play time. I wanted Janay. I had the podium, it was my show. Let me be the first to tell the reader, if you haven't noticed already I'm a hell of a guy. Very Different.

One of the girls asked me my name. Me, not thinking and not ready for that one, said my name was Spencer. The reason I said Spencer is because that was the farthest thing from a gangster name. What gangsta you know by the name of Spencer? They asked us where we from and what did we do. I know she only asked what we do because I kept flashing that big dope-boy knot every time I bought our drinks. I had a mouth full of golds too, so I told them hoes I was from Florida and my pops owned a roofing company. One of the girls chimed in and claimed she knew we were from Florida. In my mind, I'm saying, *shorty you too smart for your own good.* Dumb bitch.

The club was closing. I shot a few slick remarks at Janay to let her know she was who I was choosing. I offered to take them to the Waffle House. They agreed. The Waffle House was right in front of our hotel on Highpoint Road.

While we were at the table they asked a thousand questions, and I'm spitting out great answers. They kept saying, "Spencer you so nice!"

I found out Janay had her own car and crib. Plus, she worked in the mall at *5-7-9*. She was a manager. Damn I'm lucky. I text Domo and told him I was cracking on Janay. If she come with me, go get a cheap room until I put it down.

Aqueena asked where we live. I pointed to the hotel and said, "We living in that room right there."

Janay automatically spoke up, "You staying in that hotel? I been living in Greensboro my whole life and never been inside there."

I told her, smiling, "It's real nice on the inside."

I cracked on Janay and told her to come hang out with me, so I can get to knew her better. She declined.

"I just met you, Spencer," she said, deflecting.

Her thirsty-ass homegirls said, "Bitch, you crazy. Spencer is nice!"

So, while they still trying to convince her, me and Janay exchanged numbers. (See, if you trying to fuck a bitch, sometimes if you make her homegirl happy then she will convince her to fuck you. Girls have more influence on girls.) I left $100 dollars on the table for the meal, thanked them for a good night, and we left.

When we got back to the room, I could finally be Long again. I had a shitload of calls from Fayetteville hoes. They wanted to know where their dick was. I told Dom that when I fucked Janay I was going to fuck the shit out of her, get house keys and car keys. He bet me before he went to sleep that I wouldn't do it. I text Janay back and forth until we went to sleep. As I drifted to sleep, I thought to myself, *this is about to be my new Fayetteville.*

The next night we did a repeat. Went and got fresh, met Janay and her crew at the club, got drunk, and back to the Waffle House.

This night Janay must have freshened up that pussy and put a lil' vinegar in her bath water because when I cracked, she was game. She came back to the room with me and Domo got a cheap hotel.

While me and Janay in the room chilling, she kept admiring the room. We end up taking a shower. When we got out, I laid down on the other bed and played it cool.

Janay said, "Why you way over there, Spencer?"

Well I've been around girls long enough to know that was my cue. I slipped in bed with Janay and touched her everywhere but her pussy. I'm a player, we don't show thirstiness, even under pressure. This Long talking to you. Let me tell you like I told you before, my dick game is serious! I'm so confident all I got to do is get it in and it's over. That's just what Janay let me do—get it in.

When I tell you I fucked shorty too good, even I had to tell myself, *boy you slanging this big, long crocked dick tonight.*

All Janay kept saying is, "Spencer... oh my gosh! What are you doing to me? I *never* been fucked like this!"

After hours of fucking, she begged me to stop. I went even harder. It was day break when I finally finished and pulled off the condom. Janay busted so many nuts she was exhausted. What Janay didn't know is, I fuck to perfection in general. The fact that I was on a mission didn't help her.

I woke up about 10 A.M. with Janay all up under me. I reminded her she had to be to work at 2 p.m. like she claimed. I left Janay in the bed while I went to take a shower.

From the bed, Janay spoke, "Spencer, how much you paying to stay at this room?"

"Why Janay, are you gonna help me?" I spit back.

"I was just asking Spencer," she replied.

I told her $250 a night.

She gasped, "Oh my gosh, Spencer, that's a lot of money to be staying at a room. How long have you been staying here?"

I told her, "A lil' over a week, but I'm looking for my own crib." I knew she was adding my pockets (lol.)

Then Janay spoke 2pac to my ears, "You don't have to stay here, you can come stay at my house."

Hold up, let me stop the book for a second. When I tell you I'm the truth, you just say truuuuuuuuuuuuueee (lol). My dick game serious, she should have said this soon as I nutted. She wasn't about to risk losing the best dick she had thus far. I was smiling on the inside, but I couldn't let her know it. I kept my game face on. Remember when Mo said, 'Long when it comes to this game you a playing motherfucker?' Well, I'm him, homie! I'm from Haymount Hill. I'm in another city putting this shit down while on the run for a body. Greensboro was my new Fayetteville. Janay was my new Dee.

I held my composure. I came down here with my dog, we a package deal. You get me, you get him too.

So, I said, "Shorty, I would love to come stay at your house, but I got Domo with me and I don't wanna be a burden on nobody."

"Spencer, he can come too. I pay the bills in that house."

Damn, this dick is good, boy! What you talking 'bout? I'm too smooth!

I text Domo and told him we in. Check us out the room, get our deposit, and I'd send him the address.

Janay pulled me up at her apartment off West Market Street in Greensboro. I peeped out the scene for any signs of drug dealing or hanging out that brought the cops. I couldn't get caught up in nobody else's bullshit. The coast was clear, so Janay took me in her apartment, showed me around, and showed me my new bed. Ashley was her roommate, but she was at work. (Ashley has a sister named Monique who I still love to death to this day.)

Janay hopped in the shower and got ready for work. Right before she was about to leave, Janay said, "Spencer you can drop me off at work. It's a house key on here so you can get back in so you won't be bored."

I dropped Janay off at work and directed Domo to the new spot.

I was backed in when Domo pulled up. He saw me and punched the steering wheel.

"Boy you the truth!" Domo said, giving props to how I put it down. I walked him upstairs to our new home. I made sure no one was in there before I spoke.

"Welcome to our new home, homie," I said.

Domo fixed us something to eat. I reminded him not to slip up and call me Long around them girls. We joked and ate right at my new house.

My dick game and my mouthpiece are so top-notch, I'll bank on that before I bank on a dollar. All I could say was, "Domo we in. Now, let's explore this new city…."

Shout out to Janay. If you are reading this, I want to tell you I was only protecting my identity, trying to conceal my past. I want you to know when I met you, you took a lot off me from what I was going through. I apologize for manipulating you, at first. I apologize to your moms to for all the lies I told her. I wish you and your family nothing but the best.

Shout out to my Fayetteville chicks that held me down when shit got real. Tiffany and all your friends. MeMe drunk ass (lol.) Shay, Renee, KeKe, Mrs. Evette, Hattie (can't forget you Hattie), Lanadia, Keshawna... I can't name everybody, so the ones I couldn't name, just know it ain't nothing but love.

Domo, if you are reading this, I love you, my nigga. You already know I'm one of a kind, homie! You a real motherfucker. We more than friends; we blood

brothers. But you need to pay me on that bet with Janay. I need that, my commissary low as fuck right now. I'm living off the land in this motherfucker. (LOL.)

Domo got 14 years in North Carolina State prison. Hold ya head homie! They making books about the shit we did.

The Hotel in Greensboro I was living in

CHAPTER 18

Exploring Greensboro

Me and Janay going hard with each other. I got her open. She never had a real gangsta in her life. She used to say all the time that I was crazy. Little did she know, I am throwed the fuck off, but I'm super intelligent.

Our favorite food spot was the *Best Diner* off of Market Street, a twenty-four-hour joint. Philly Steak N Cheese with fries. It was right down the street from her crib. I ended up bagging the white girl waitress that worked there. Come to find out, she had her own condo and her family was rich. She just worked there to have extra money.

I started fucking the white girl. She let me come to her condo when I got ready. She had a dog name Mately.

One morning I woke up, the dog was licking my face. She gonna look over at me and say,

"Mately, Spencer don't won't no early morning kisses."

Bitch, my name ain't Spencer, and I don't want no early morning or late-night kisses from a dog. That's what I was thinking.

I knew fucking this white girl was gonna be a problem. I shouldn't have fucked her. She worked at a spot I went to every day, and I didn't know too many spots. I would hang out there while Janay was at work.

One night, Me and Janay went to Best Diner. I tried to go somewhere else, but I couldn't. The white girl in there was mean mugging and texting me crazy shit. So, when Janay and I made it outside, she knew I fucked that white girl. Somehow women just know.

She bitched about it for hours. "Spencer, I know you ain't fucking that white girl."

I kept denying it, telling her I wouldn't fuck that girl and we go there all the time. I don't even like white people, I insisted. She ended up telling me I couldn't go back to *Best Diner* without her going with me. I fucked her good that night and put her to sleep.

Dom was getting plenty of pussy down there also. He was fucking Janay's roommate and so many hoes. We were breezing through that motherfucker. Since one truth will buy you a thousand lies, I introduced Janay to my cousin. This way, whenever I didn't come home, I would say I stayed with my cousin.

By then, it was time to expand. I had Janay show me around the city. She showed me all the roads that had roadblocks on them, so I could avoid them. (I'm far from a Dummy.) After that, I was moving around. I used to go to Jack's Diner or Wendover a lot by this time.

One night, I took Janay out to the club. I wanted her to show me who was who. She showed me people as we kept going out. One by one, she pointed out the robbers, the hustlers, the real money getters, and so on and so on. In order to move around, you have to know who is who. I did a good job too.

I went to the mall a lot, and before you knew it, the mall had my number and would call me when a new shipment came in. I'm talking everybody was getting to know Spencer.

I picked me a good gas station to always stop at. I don't do Arab stores, too much shit go on at them. I was trying to be low. That's my word, if you from Greensboro, ask your man Q. Diddy that be throwing the parties how we had Ménage on Thursday nights. They didn't even know my name. I had a long beard so they just called me P. Troy to the stage. Me and Dom would go throw money on all the college bitches shaking their asses one by one. They loved us!

Hoes started fucking with me now. I had a flock of hoes up there just like Fayetteville. The only difference was, I was Spencer up there and Long back home. Like Dee back home, Janay was my main spot up there. My boo. It was wild to be fucking all these different girls, hearing them all say, *"Spencer, why you fucking me like this???"*

One night, I was drunk, fucking this bitch, and she called me Spencer. I was about to check her like, *Bitch who did you just call me?* Then, I remembered that I was Spencer and just kept on fucking the hoe.

Janay is super loving me now. She introduced me to her mom and her father. Her mom loved me and used to ask about the roofing business all the time. I would always respond that things are going great. I even had a goddaughter up there, this little girl named Noodles. I used to buy her what she wanted, and she still remembers me to this day. Instead of Godfather, she used to call me granddaddy Spencer. (LMAO.)

This was my home now. I had someone take my grandma a brand-new prepaid phone so we could communicate. I had to check on my heart.

I was still getting money in the city, but now I had brought work up here too. I used to be cooking up in Janay's house and she would come into the kitchen talking about what is it gonna do when you finish whipping it? I tell ya, this girl was as green as the Netherlands.

I met some dudes out of Burlington who wanted to cop from me. At first, I was gonna bring them the work but decided against it. I didn't have a gun up there because I never knew when them people was gonna run up on me. My mind was the gun then. You only needed a real gun when you put yourself in dangerous environments. I knew these dudes didn't know me and might would've tired me and I would've hated to pack up and move to Charlotte next.

Well anyways, I sent the work with Janay to work at *5.7.9*. She took 9 ounces in her purse. Janay was the manager, so when they met me in the store I took the money in a changing stall, counted it, and put it in a bg. I walked out and whispered in Janay's ear to put that in there for them. She gonna have the gall to ask me if I was coming home that night. (I guess she wanted her treat for being a good girl.) (LOL) I told her, I'd call her.

She snarled at me, "You make me sick, Spencer, with yo black ass!"

I walked past the dudes dolo, then told them it was in the stall. I continued to meet them there, plus my other flow I was accumulating up there. Everything going smooth.

My mind is a motherfucker. I'm 23 at the time. No army, no clique, just me and my nigga thuggin', going hard, finding our way through life. You can't outthink me!

I became known fast. Not only did I move into another city, I made my presence known fast. I went and purchased a drop-top Benz off of Market Street from the luxury car dealership, just before you get to the car wash going towards Spring Garden. Now I'm running around this motherfucker, top back, hitting bad bitches.

This one bitch I was fucking used to drive ambulances. She was bad as shit. I had my Fayetteville chicks coming up there, fucking them in rooms. I would even go back to my hood and go straight to my grandma's house like I wasn't on the run, like my picture wasn't all over this motherfucker. You think I'm lying, don't you? I don't front. Ain't nothing gonna stop me from going to see my grandma. I wanted her to see me to know I was still in one piece.

They should have put me on a *wanted thot* page. Everywhere I went, I got my dick sucked. I was just moving like the gangsta I am. Niggas respected it and bitches loved it.

One day, I was in the club in Greensboro. I was by myself with the top back in VIP. I see this fine bitch. I approached her and found out her name was Erika. She was from Winston Salem. I introduced myself as Darrell. (Spencer was played out. Plus, she was from another city.) At the time, I'm already fucking this bad bitch named Tia from High Point and she knew me by Darrell. If you don't know about Greensboro, High Point, and Winston Salem, they're all three cities, fifteen minutes from each other, regardless of which way you go. So, the Highpoint and Winston Salem hoes knew me as Darrell, and Greensboro knew me as Spencer. So, when I told her my name was Darrell, I went hard on her. She was fine and soft as baby powder, hands down. She had freckles on her cheeks, light skin, and long natural hair. Plus, she was thicker than a King size snicker.

We started kicking it after that. Man listen, the pussy was amazing. Shorty had that wet box and knew how to slang that slit. Pussy and head ain't turning Longhead out, but shorty head game was even more serious than the pussy. She used to wake me up sucking this dick. For her, it was just like the rest of the girls, except she was saying,

"*Darrell*, what are you doing to me? I ain't ever been fucked like this!"

Let me stop the book for a second... these dudes must don't be fucking these hoes right. Either that, or all of them lying to me. Or my dick is the truth (no homo.) I promise, she said the same thing they all said.

Erika put her claws in me. I started feeling shorty, and it wasn't because she was bad and a freak. I fucked plenty of bad bitches that was freaks. That simp shit be for them dudes that be hitting ducks all their life and can't climb into these type of holes.

Before you knew it, I was living with Erika in her apartment in Kernesville, North Carolina, right outside Winston Salem. I told you, I know how to change my appearances and character. It was always, yes ma'am, no ma'am. So, when Erika introduced me to her mom, she fell in love with me. Erika's mom liked me so much she would cook me Sunday dinners of whatever I wanted. I even offered to cut Erika's mom grass on Saturdays. Erika was my boo.

One night, Janay caught me and Erika in the club. She tried to swing on me and Erika wanted to fight her. I knew I couldn't let this go down. I pulled Janay to the side and told her to go home, and I'll be there shortly.

Janay said, "Spencer, if you don't come, I'ma fuck you up!"

Erika waved me over to where she was and said, "Darrell, I'm ready to go."

I told her okay and returned to Janay. Janay swore that if I didn't come home she was going to fuck me up.

It was funny. I'm way up there on the run for murder, living under fake names, moving slick, destroying people lives. I was putting this shit down so hard I had to laugh at myself. One girl was in love with me calling me Spencer, the other was in love with me calling me Darrell. Mo said it best, I was a playing motherfucker.

Erika didn't let me leave out the house that night. Me and Janay relationship was falling apart; I was with Erika now. People always knew I was smart, they told me that all the time, but they never knew to what extent.

To sum it all up, I play all positions in this baseball game—not just the drug game, but any game when I'm playing.

Whoever is reading this book, I wanna let you know the reason I'm so known in my city. How can you miss my name in a conversation? How you from Fayetteville and miss speaking on Longhead in a conversation? If you talking about jacking niggas, you gotta mention me, my nigga. If you wanna talk about niggas who put this shit down in other people's cities, and niggas who put motherfuckers in their place when they get out of line, you gotta mention me. If you wanna talk about stunting, hitting all the bad chicks, riding luxury, you gotta mention me. If you wanna talk about the realest nigga from the city, you gotta mention my name, my nigga. Should I say more? What more can I say?

Shout out to Monique from Greensboro. I love you, baby. My dawg for life.

CHAPTER 19
The Shootings

I know what you are thinking: this motherfucker wild as shit down there in Carolina. This is the thing though, life put you in situations all the time. It's when you can think that you'll come out on top. My ability to think is my strong point. How do you think I made it this far? Oh yeah, you gotta have nuts too. Don't tuck your tail, give it to them bitch-ass niggas exactly how they ask for it.

By now, Dee had gotten a low-key apartment in the super cut. We all know her door was open to me when I would come to Fayetteville, no matter the time. I would have Mrs. Judy's daughter, Tab, from Haymount Hill meet me in Spring Lake and switch cars with me. Tab a gangsta, we grew up together. She was game and trustworthy. I would let her drive my Benz and I would drive her low-key car to run around the city.

One day I'm in Fayetteville real low, and I ran into Black Vaughn from Savoy Heights. Now, if you from Fayetteville, you heard of Black Vaughn. He's a real snake. Gonna rob you and shoot you—just my type of guy. I'm from the slums, that's right up my alley. We linked up and I pulled up at my man's Irk house in Savoy Heights. (Before he died, his mama gave him that house.) My picture was posted everywhere down there. I'm right there in the hood while every police in the city looking for me. I ain't ducking shit, homie. Plus, I forgot to mention I ran like a deer, so I'm cocky on my feet.

I met Black Vaughn over Irk's house. We were in the living room and Black Vaughn said,

"Everybody and their daddy looking for you. I know you could use a nice lick for about two-hundred grand."

Now hold up for a second, I'm from Haymount Hill. For two-hundred grand, he going in the trunk in broad daylight! I knew Black Vaughn *knew* me personally. He wouldn't play with me. Or would he?

So, while Black Vaughn was telling his story, my man Irk added his two cents, "Hell yeah, when y'all finish, look out for me."

Irk was a good kid, he wasn't with this. He just the cool dude from the hood.

Black Vaughn's mouth was so slick he belonged in New York somewhere. When he finished talking this motherfucker really put his con game down. I'd be a lie if I told you Black Vaughn didn't talk me out my car keys because he did. He claimed he was going to prepare for the lick. I knew Black Vaughn knew not to play with me like everybody else, so I gave him Tab's keys to her car and Black Vaughn took off.

Black Vaughn stayed gone for a while. It started to get late and I was in a safe spot, but I was ready to go. I start calling Black Vaughn and he didn't pick up. Then I got pissed. I sent him a text and asked him if he lost his mind. I ended up having somebody come get me from Irk's house. I called this nigga's brother and told him I was gonna fuck him and Black Vaughn up on sight.

He went to copping pleas, "I'm 'bout to find him right now, Long."

Damn, I had been gone that long they thought I forgot how to put this shit down? I'm motherfucking Longhead from Haymount Hill, the heart of Clark Street.

I called Tab to break the bad news to her. Either way, Tab had to still give me my car back. I had to make it back to Kernesville where my old lady was waiting on me.

When I told Tab, she said, "LORD what am I going to drive, brother? Why would he do that, he know you gone fuck him up?"

Tab had her homegirl follow her to our meeting spot. Before I pulled off, I told Tab I was going to handle that, I just didn't have time tonight.

She said, "Oh trust me, I know you gone get him, brother. He know too."

When I made it to Kernesville, I text and called Black Vaughn in the parking lot. I still couldn't believe it. This nigga took a car from Longhead. (LMAO.) This motherfucker was ready to be dressed out to sees JESUS.

So, I'm chilling with Erika waiting to eat the food she cooked when my phone rang. It was Black Vaughn. I told Erika I had to take this call and stepped outside. I sat in my car so no one could hear me talking. I never said Black Vaughn was soft, he will bust that gun and rob, but he knew better to fuck with me. I'm not going for it, homie, for nothing.

"Hello, man where you at with that car?" I asked him. "I'ma fuck you up," I told him.

This nigga laughed and said, "You can't even come out like that. And since you are threatening my brother, I'm keeping this car. See me when you see me!" Then he hung up.

I was so pissed, I was in my own car punching shit, snatching shit out the glove compartments, going crazy. That's when I saw Erika come to the door looking for me.

I calmed down, opened the door, and called out to her, "I'm coming baby!"

She yelled back, "Darrell, hurry up."

I looked in the rear-view mirror and took a deep breath. *You are Darrell right now. Straighten up.* Going back to the house, I kept repeating it, reminding myself that I was Darrell.

The whole night I thought of Black Vaughn. I couldn't believe this nigga. I couldn't shake his disrespect from my mind, and trust me, you don't wanna be on a nigga like me mind.

A few days later, Black Vaughn left the car in Walmart parking lot with the keys in it. He called me and said, "Your car in Walmart, pussy. Go get it" Then he hung up.

I told Tab where her car was and collected my thoughts.

I didn't know what was wrong with this motherfucker, but I was sure to find out. I was in the Ville looking for him hard. Haymount Hill is my hood. I am Haymount Hill, you think I ain't going back because I'm on the run? I didn't get a chance to find Black Vaughn, but this is the story I got.

It was late night at an afterhours spot beside Crazy Dave's off Owen Drive. Black Vaughn was walking in the parking lot hollering at hoes. He was bent over in a girl's car talking when somebody came up behind him and wet his ass down. (lmao.)

Hold up, this shit wild! When I heard this, I said, boy somebody caught Black Vaughn before I could have caught him slipping good. They rushed him to the hospital where death was knocking at his front door. His main artery was hit, and he almost bled out.

Black Vaughn didn't tell the police I shot him. From my understanding, he didn't know who shot him. He did make a video and put it on YouTube. I forgot the name of it or I would give it to you, so you can check it out. He was laid in the hospital, fucked up, talking about, *I know you shot me boy. I'ma get you pussy.* Barely escaped death and still talking shit.

I was laughing when somebody put me on it. I said Black Vaughn got 9 lives. After being laid up in the hospital for a while, he got out. He was fucked up though. If you are asking me, he won't be taking no cars no more. This nigga had a metal rod coming out one of his legs that looked like a pull up bar. (LMAO.)

He told me he knew I shot him.

Tab called me and said, "Brother, somebody got Black Vaughn; it wasn't you, Brother?"

With a smirk, I told her, "Sis, you know I don't play with guns."

This shit was wild! Not only was I on the run for murder and living a double life in another city, every time somebody got killed or shot and they didn't know who did it, they were screaming my name. I understand I'm Long, but I can't be in all these places at once. I know I'm a slick moving nigga, but some shit was just wild.

When the kid, Money, from Bunce Road got shot, the story was that I waited outside his house. When he got in his car, I ran up and hit him in the chest, then slid off. That's the story I got. Now this nigga Money heard of me; who don't know Longhead from the Hill?

So, what did he do? He went to screaming I shot him in his chest. When I first heard it, I brushed it off because there was so much being blamed on me around this time it wasn't funny.

I wasn't tripping until this dude hit me up from the next town over.

He said, "Big Homie, this nigga named Money just offered me a half of brick to kill you. That nigga crazy if he think I'm going against you."

Now to be honest, the nigga he went and got bust that pistol, but I'm Longhead bitch! When y'all gonna learn? Your hitters respect *me.* I'm in the streets. They don't respect you or your money; they basically telling you to keep your money and find him your fucking self.

So, I told dude to give me his number and he gave it to me—and told me he would hit money tonight for me. (LMAO.) He tried to pay a nigga to hit me, and his hitta turned around and offered to hit him for free for me.

The reason they respect me is simple. I don't link up or get nobody to do shit for me. I'm a hands-on motherfucker. I'm the one you gonna see when it's time.

So, I called him and he answered. I said, "What's up? This Long, that money you offered up wasn't enough. Now you gonna need it for your own arrangements." Then I hung up.

If I was thinking, and not in my feelings, I would have extorted this sucker. I'm for real with this shit, homie. You talking about killing me, I get tunnel vision and don't see shit. He can bank on him getting a visitor, and it might not be who he is looking for.

So, my phone rang about thirty minutes later. I answered aggressively.

"Who this?" I barked.

The other voice said, "Long this, 4W from the Murk. I fuck with you."

So, I said, "What's up?"

He said, "Long, you done broke up my card game."

I knew 4W ran a gambling house for all the money-getters in the city. So, I said, "4, what are you talking 'bout, homie?"

He said, "Man, Money just left outta here crying, talking 'bout you gone kill him. And go get his mama out her house because you gone kill her too."

I said, "4, you mean to tell me this nigga was crying? And told you to go get his mom out her house?"

"Yeah fam."

"Do this nigga know who I am 4, and what I'll do to him?"

"Long, I know what you about, fam. And money do too. It was a nigga at the card table that told him, 'You beefing with Long, know that boy don't fuck around.' Plus, fam, they say you just shot him in the chest; he lucky to be alive right now, so he knows. He even told me he apologizes for whatever he done to you."

I told 4, "I'ma call the nigga."

He said, "Yeah, do that, fam, and let these niggas live out here, Long. We know you the truth."

When I got off the phone with 4W, I was thinking, *He know this shit real, what the fuck he talking 'bout killing me for? He knows he lucky to be alive, whoever shot him.*

So I called him back. He picked up on the first ring, "Man, why you telling people to go get your mama out the house? I don't do mamas, homie; I get my target."

He said, "Man Long, I promise I ain't got no beef with you. Why you tried to kill me? I ain't ever did nothing to you. They say you got heart, you the one to watch out for. They say you just like me."

Hold up, did this nigga just say I was just like him? (LMAO.) We ain't nothing alike. He had a little reputation, they said he shot a gun or two, but that shit don't hold no weight when you dealing with Long from Haymount Hill.

I checked him and told him don't be talking reckless on my phone, talking about I tried to kill him. He ended up apologizing, so I killed it for him. He might have been tough to them, but to me, he was soft as cotton. Shit, let me even *think* you shot me in my chest. Matter fact, you ain't even got the nuts to pull out on me, homie. He didn't want no beef.

Where was my life headed? One day, somebody gonna get the nuts to kill ole' Longhead. I ain't tripping though. Until then, I'm gonna go harder than a motherfucker, put suckers in their place, make fuck niggas pay homage, salute all the real niggas, and fuck all the bad bitches—no pillow talking though.

My hoes used to tell me, I heard you did such and such. I'd tell the bitch, I ain't did shit. If she wanna be in the streets, get a pack and a pistol. It's dangerous out there; that bitch won't get put under pressure and do me in. Fuck that! If they ever ask her, she don't know shit for real! (LOL.) I'm too real for this shit.

Black Vaughn, if you are reading this, you knew damn well not to play with me like that. You know me, even though you gave the car back, you violated big-time. When I was super young, my uncle Kojack said, no exceptions. Anybody cross you... well you know the rest.

Money, if you reading this, you know I ain't lying. I'm 200% accurate. If you feel some type of way, there ain't shit you can do about it. I am him, homie. You know it. I tell it how it happened. Let me hear you ever talking crazy again, you won't get so lucky. Stay out my lane, homie.

CHAPTER 20
How the Dice Roll

Here I go, like I told you, when shit going too sweet you have to be aware.

Shit was going sweet, far as my run game. I had multiple run-ins with the cops, but like I've stated, I ran like a deer. They couldn't fuck with me on a broken leg.

I remember a few times Dee had to come scoop me up. Like when they had me boxed in at about 4 in the morning while I was in an unfamiliar hood. Let me be the first to tell you, I didn't have to be on Haymount Hill to get away. I was hiding under a shed in somebody backyard. I had my cellphone, so I directed Dee to me by phone. She came and grabbed me, and we rode right past the Marshals. I was slick. I also had GOD on my side. How could I lose? (Dee, damn shorty, who are you? If you had a dick you would be my right-hand man.)

I was back playing Fayetteville hard again. Dudes was getting too comfortable. I even popped up in clubs and had everybody shitting bricks. (LMAO.) These dudes were petrified of me. How could I blame them?

It was a December day. I was chilling at Mo's house, holding a normal conversation, while we watched Western movies. Next thing I knew, the door exploded off the hinges. Big white boys poured in with assault rifles, wearing *US Marshals* vests, screaming, "Get the fuck down motherfucker!"

I laid down, they secured the house, and Mo remained on the couch. Then, they started doing what they do best, yelling *stop resisting* and beat my ass. I guess they beat me for making them work so hard. They handcuffed me, and before we walked out, one of them threw a rifle in Mo's face.

He asked Mo, "Do you know who the fuck this man is?"

Mo looked at that motherfucker and said, "Hell naw, player, I don't know him."

What the US Marshalls didn't know is they missed everything. It was all in the ceiling, up high like Mo taught me. Boy, Mo was a motherfucker!

They rushed me to the post office into a holding cell. My hoes kept calling. They would answer my phone and say, "You won't see Longhead for a long time."

Jonisha, one of my boos back then, cried when they told her that. Shorty fucked with me the long way.

So, who quickly rushed down there? Some motherfuckers who been waiting for this day to come: homicide detectives. Being that the Marshals caught me, I was in their custody. The detectives had to ask them would I speak with them. I told the Marshals, *Fuck no, take me to my cell. I'm sleepy now; it's been a long run.* They did.

The Homicide had me charged with Bobby's murder, but wanted to accuse me of about three more murders, and multiple shootings. I told you, they were putting everything on me. I was living in Greensboro!

One guy, they claimed I blew his brains out and dumped him in the graveyard. Another dude, his bitch, Teeka, found him dead in his house, called the cops and told the police Tab set it up and I killed him. Bitch get the fuck out of here! She was jealous that Tab's sister Bay Bay was fucking him. But why this bitch tell them I did it? I would have done something bad to that anorexic bitch. To this day, the police still be running up on Tab telling her she needs to tell on me.

This other guy from Ponderosa got killed. They claimed I did that too. Not only were they blaming me, they are telling these people I'm the prime suspect. All these murders are still unsolved to this day. They had blamed so many shootings on me it was sad. They claimed I shot a lot of people, I just wasn't identified. My thing is, if I wasn't identified how the fuck y'all saying me?

News spread about me getting locked up, and I could hear the suckers: *'They got ole' Longhead last night.' 'I'm glad they got that motherfucker; he was doing too much.' 'What the fuck that nigga thought he was?'* (LMAO.) Don't be suckers all your life, you know what you signed up for.

I called my grandma when I got to the back, "Well baby, they got me," I said.

Instantly she replied, "Don't worry about that, GOD got you. You will be outta there before you know it, just watch, son. Have I ever lied to you?"

"No ma'am, Grandma. I'm not worried because I know I haven't done nothing."

"I knew you was down there already," she revealed.

"How did you know that grandma?"

"My buddy Mo came over," she shared. My grandma loved Mo. "He came over here crying and said, 'they got our boy, Mrs. May.' I told Mo, don't worry, GOD got him," she said.

She said Mo replied, "I know Mrs. May, but they don't make them like Long no more. I know he ain't nothing but 24 years old, but Mrs. May he is the real deal."

When Grandma relayed me the message from my mentor, I had to smile to myself. I told Grandma I loved her and I'd see her soon.

Grandma got so much faith in GOD, it could be the worst situation, everything looking bad, and she gonna say you can't see what she can see. She always speaks positive. I never met anyone as strong as this woman. She's outstanding!

I was sitting in the County Jail in December, right before Christmas. I was apprehended exactly one year from the day they gave me this charge. It was time to call my hoes and get in bid mode. I had to call my woman, Erika.

Now I knew Erika was wondering where the fuck I was; she was loving me. So I called and she accepted.

"Hello, who is this?" Erika said.

"Erika, it's me, Darrell baby."

"Darrell, oh my gosh! What are you doing in jail? Baby, I have some things to tell you! Darrell, what is it? Do I need to come get you?"

I swallowed the lump in my throat and dropped my truth. "Baby you can't come get me, I don't have a bond."

Erika gasped, "Where are you Darrell?" I told her I was in Fayetteville. "What are you doing in Fayetteville?"

"It's a long story, Baby."

"What did you do Darrell?"

"I didn't do nothing Erika, but I'm charged with murder."

She started crying, "Oh my God, Darrell. I'm coming to see you. I gotta call my mama and tell her. She's gonna be sad; she loves you Darrell!" Erika said between her tears.

Let me remind y'all, me and Erika was *together.* Her family had accepted me. Plus, she was fine as shit. I dedicated Erika in my book because she played a major role in my life back then also. She's worth every page I'm writing on. When Erika said she was coming to see me, I told her I had one more thing to tell her.

"What is it Darrell?"

"Darrell isn't my real name."

When I revealed my biggest secret to her is when I realized how much I crushed this girl. She was in love with me. It's like I betrayed her. She was crushed. Erika didn't even give me a chance to explain. She hung up and refused to pick the phone back up that night. I thought maybe she was mad and needed to calm down.

I was wrong.

The next day when I called her phone was disconnected. She got a new number.

All the other hoes I had rode for me. Janay found out who I was and didn't care. She drove and visited me. Of course, my Fayetteville hoes were supporting me. I wasn't *hoeless,* but I was empty on the inside. I'm a real nigga, my nigga. All I could think of was Erika. I was really feeling shorty. I know her family panicked, like, *Erika who did you bring in our home?* She already acted like a white girl. When I lost Erika, I felt like I lost all my hoes at once. She was worth my flock.

While I was sitting in my cell, I was talking to this young nigga named Keyontay out of Raeford, North Carolina through the vents. He was 17 years old with a body. I took a liking to lil' homie. (He ended up getting 25 years.) My lil' homie had them hoes on deck!

So, while we talking I hear a nigga say, "Long come to the door. Man, you won't believe who it is: Black Vaughn."

(LOL.) Ole' Black Cobra. Soon as he heard my name, this motherfucker screamed to the top floor, "Why you shoot me!?"

I yelled right back, "Quit saying that shit out loud, homeboy!"

He told me to come to his door when I came out. He was still fucked up. If you know about our county jail, I was on the top floor while he was on the bottom. When one tier went in, the other one came out. Don't think I'm just in the streets, I'm gonna fight too, homie. I do it all! I'm from Haymount Hill, I ain't ducking shit but a diseased bitch.

I went to his door and he kept asking me why I shot him. It kinda reminded me of New Jack City when Ice T said, *Oh shit! That's the kid I shot*. (Lol.) Nah, I'm joking.

So, I told him, "Man, you tripping dog. The walls can talk in this motherfucker."

I noted that he was barely making it around. He was fucked up.

He then yelled, "Go get the motherfucking nurse!"

I said, "For what?"

"You shot me motherfucker! I'm in pain."

So, I went and got the nurse for him. If I could make this shit up, I would have a hell of an imagination.

I sat in the County just waiting to prove my innocence. I got in Bid Mode and my months started to fly by. Stuck in the County Jail once again, another mission on Longhead's plate, and I thought of Erika.

Erika, if you are reading this... I know I broke your heart. I know you didn't get a chance to get my name. Erika, from the bottom of my pimpin' heart, I apologize to you and your mom. I was only trying to protect my identity. I never meant to tell you no lies. If I could rewind time, I would have told you the truth.

I ran across a guy from Winston Salem and he described you to a T. He asked me how I knew you. I told him you were my girlfriend. This lame asked me if I was fucking you. Then he said that he always wanted to fuck you. (LMAO.) Dudes be lame. I should have told him you have no game. He told me you were modeling in ATL. I knew you were fine as shit. Go for your goals, shorty. I salute you. Our demise was all my fault. If I ever see you again, I'm gonna blush super hard.

It's been almost 10 years since I've seen Erika. Last time I spoke to her she hung up the phone. Maybe I'm chasing a ghost but I, at least, wanna see her again in life and apologize to her face for causing confusion in her life. Feel me? I'm just a real nigga, not thirsty or desperate.

Next chapter... Don't nothing seem to shock me at this point, but this shit might shock you what's about to hit these pages. Keep reading, you'll see...

One of Fayetteville's most-wanted fugitives arrested

Posted December 19, 2008

FAYETTEVILLE, N.C. — A Fayetteville man was arrested Thursday and charged with the shooting death of a man a year ago, authorities said.

Larry Donnell Everett, 24, of 1110 Clark St., was arrested at an apartment in the 600 block of Oakridge Avenue by members of the U.S. Marshals Service Violent Fugitive Task Force. He was charged with first-degree murder, attempted first-degree murder, assault with a deadly weapon with intent to kill, conspiracy to commit murder and shooting into an occupied vehicle.

Everett is one of four men charged in the Dec. 19, 2007, shooting death of Bobby Eugene Clemmons and was considered one of Fayetteville's most-wanted fugitives.

Clemmons, 23, was left at the emergency entrance to Highsmith Rainey Hospital after being shot, and he later died, police said.

Investigators said Everett and the other suspects fired an assault rifle, a shotgun and a handgun into the car in which Clemmons was riding.

David William Covington, 24, of 204 Brinkley St.; Kajuan Kenneth Toles, 25, of 827-A Orange St.; and Ricky Lavelle Martin Jr., 20, of 289 Ingram St., also were charged with Clemmons' death.

CHAPTER 21
Bizarre

I tell you the truth, I was sitting in jail in July of 2009. This C.O. bitch I was cool with walked from the front and came to my dorm. She came over my intercom screaming with excitement.

"Mr. Everett!"

I said, "Calm down, baby. I'm still here."

"Boy, do you know they dismissed your *Murder* and *Shooting into an Occupied Vehicle* charges?" She was reading off a slip.

I yelled, "Fuck yeah! I'm motherfucking Longhead. I told you I ain't did shit! Pop my door, let me out this motherfucker."

God is good. I went by every real nigga door and told them I'm out this motherfucker. I went by Keyontay's door and told him I was going to catch up with him.

I'm a real nigga, my nigga. Every time Keyontay hit my line and needed that bread, I sent it *and* I met him in jail. My lil' homie, Rio, just came in on a double homicide. I coached lil' homie. That was my dog; he ended up getting 5 years. They dropped his murders.

The C.O. called me to her desk and asked, "What are you doing when you get out?"

Oh, she was thinking about some dick. Girl bye! I gotta get back to the money.

I asked her where my dog was, Quan.

"He over there packing his stuff too. They gone let y'all out one by one. They knew y'all would be too loud if y'all walked out together," she explained.

I said, "I don't give a fuck, as long as they let us out."

Come to find out, the boy Buck from Massey Hill ended up telling them people the truth—that he didn't see who was shooting. So, without their only fake witness who recanted his statement, they had to let us free. My kidnapping charge was dismissed also. I was a free man again after all the shit they tried to put on me (liar you.) I'm Longhead. Haymount Hill. Clark Street. Real niggas salute me. At least you know we haven't gone extinct.

I went straight to the Hill to see my grandma. I gave her a hug and a kiss.

She said, "Son, what did I tell you? You wouldn't be down there long. God is real, son."

"I know, Grandma."

Quan kicked it with Grandma while I hopped in the shower. When I finished, we hopped in the car and pulled off.

As we left, grandma yelled out, "Be careful out there, son.

"I will, baby. I love you."

I blew so much money on the run, balling out, I was fucked up. I needed a come-up fast. I hated to do it, but I had to. Before I made a move I was just watching the whole scene to see what's my best move. I was hungry, not thirsty. I was trying to get that money for real for real.

There was a lil' nigga from Savoy Heights named Justo. He came to me—I'm the Big Homie—and told me his mom's boyfriend be having a lot of pounds of weed. I told him I had to have them. I asked where the dude was. He told me if his mama see me, she gonna know what time it is. Make a long story short, he had 6 pounds left, so we ordered them. I got a lil' nigga named Shine Mack from Savoy Heights to walk in Justo's mom's house and take them.

It was simple. I knew he didn't need any help. I backed in the driveway listening to 2pac until he walked out with the bag. I gave him 1 pound for his services.

The weed was some popcorn mid. I took the 5 pounds and sold them for $4,500. I had a stack in the cut and added that to it. So, I got $5,500 now. I went and got 6 ounces of soft (the prices were fucked up back in '09.) See, one thing about Longhead, he's not ashamed to admit when he fucked up. I will tell girls and all, no fronting over here. I don't mind because I know I got a million dollar mind inside a gangsta's body.

Me and Justo headed to the kitchen with 6 ounces of soft. I whipped them shits to 12 ounces of straight garbage. It had to go though.

The thing is, every man makes his own decisions and choices. I gave Justo a choice. I told him I'm going for the stars. He could roll with me or he could take his 6 ounces, and we go our separate ways. He was young; he took his 6 wrong and went his own way. Well, I took my 6, hit the block, and went the fuck off!

When hustling garbage, you gotta have a mouth piece with it. It sells faster. I went by Mo's house and told him I'm about to take off again. He told me he already knew how I was coming.

If I'm lying I'm flying, in thirty days I was worth fifty grand from just going hard every day. For those of you who get distracted with clubs, bitches, and rental cars, this type of grind don't count for you. This consists of not showering, wearing the same clothes, coming out the house with 20 dollars (just enough for food), no pussy, no hoes—straight grind mode.

In less than 60 days, I was worth almost a one-hundred grand.

I remember sitting in Mo's house taking a brief break. I shared my progress with Mo and he started laughing. "I'ma say this until I leave this world, Longhead. When it comes to this game, you a playing motherfucker," Mo said. "The average nigga in the streets ain't ready for what you put down. I seen you take 6 ounces and put it on about a 100 grand in less than 60 days. I know I taught you a lot Longhead, but you taught Mo a lot too, my nigga. They ain't ready for you."

That damn Mo called it how he saw it. I'm straight hustling, no robbing. I told you, I'm a hustler by nature and a Jack Boy because I can be.

So, as I'm getting money, I'm staying in my lane. I just got out of jail so I'm chilling out, just relaxing. Remember what I said that when things are going too perfect, something ain't right? Well, after you read this chapter, you will see why I say that.

One day I'm on the phone with Jonisha telling her about them *swell ups* in jail. She wanted me to make her one, so I agreed to come over. Jonisha's butt was so big back then you needed a horse dick to control it. I had what she needed.

When I got close to her house I stopped by the store to get the noodles, chips, crackers, and a sausage. I was about to hook this bad boy up.

At the cash register I was the 3rd person in line. Three Black males walked in. I'm from the streets, so my instincts kicked in and I'm watching my surroundings. One walked to the bathroom and one walked to the beer section. (I could see him in that big mirror up in the corner of the store.) One came and stood right by me. I never saw these dudes a day in my life. He was drunk I could tell. So, dude standing beside me while I'm in line was on the phone. I sensed something so I'm trying to pay for my snack and get the fuck out of there.

Hold up, if you one of those dudes who get drunk talking reckless, watch how this play out and you should stop.

So, whoever this dude on the phone with must have asked him what he was doing. This nigga gonna say, "Nothing baby, I'm 'bout drunk, ready to fuck a nigga up."

When he said that, my radar went up. I looked him straight in his eyes. Now this dude looking at me, talking. You know, since I just got out of jail I'm chilling, but if they wanted me to do it to them, I would've. But only if they wanted me to.

Now, I'm second in line about to put my shit on the counter. Dude walked up on me and said, "Aye homeboy, let me skip you."

Man listen, I said I was chilling, but did this nigga just walk up on me and ask to skip me? I put my shit on the counter to go next like I was in line to go.

His homie buying the beer came up and barked, "What's up?"

This nigga said, "Nothing, but these suckers out here fronting."

Now it's late night, we the only people in here. By now, he said, "I'm ready to fuck a nigga up."

He said it without talking directly to me, but I been around a long time, long enough to know this motherfucker was talking to Longhead. Now, readers, I just got out the county jail not even four month ago. I know these dudes ain't know me. I didn't have no strap on me. Yeah, I'm Longhead, but I come with sense. Mind you, I never seen these dudes a day in my life.

The third dude came out the bathroom and joined the three-man army. They followed me out the store and started shouting out, *Villa Gang Trilla Gang* or some shit. I couldn't even understand them. They were making gun shots with their mouths, all type of weirdo shit. I ignored them for the most part, these guys was looking for trouble. Honestly, I didn't know why these dudes was fucking with me. Was I scared? Fuck no, my nigga! I'm a gangsta my nigga by myself without the camera. I told myself these dudes drunk so they got a pass.

I hopped in the car to head to Jonisha's house. I pulled off and they pulled out behind me. Then, they swerved right in front of me and cut me off. So, when they went left, I went right, still trying to avoid trouble. As I'm turning in Jonisha's gated community, I pushed in the code. As the gate raised up these dudes pulled up on the side of me hanging out the window with a gun, screaming out that same shit, *trilla gang villa gang* or whatever.

I hit the deck! They pulled up under the gate and took my turn. My window was still rolled down. I heard them laughing and saying, *That bitch ass nigga don't want no problems*.

Little did they know, now I wanted a problem. Bitch, if the police out here when I get back, I'm gonna kill you boy. I punched the steering wheel and snatched the rearview mirror off the glass. I wanted a problem. Bitch, you pulled a gun on me when I tried to go the other way. I'm gonna kill you boy.

I went and switched cars, and this is what I prayed on the way back:

God, PLEASE let them be over there when I get back! Please GOD.

Guess who I'm riding with? I'm dolo motherfucker; I don't need no clique, faggot. Just me and my real lil' homie, he been begging me not to put him down. I got chill bumps writing this because these guys done fucked up. If they wasn't there when I got back, I didn't know who they were so I didn't know where to find them.

Make a long story short, that same hood was in the newspaper the next day. Two people got shot the fuck up but they lived. I'm still trying to figure out was that the dudes that did that to me. If it was, then good for them. It sounded like them from the way the newspaper explained it. I'm from the heart of the streets, I wonder why it wasn't three people shot instead of two? Their loud mouth homie probably was running for dear life. All that mouth... put my dick in it and close it.

I wonder who all they fucked with that night? (LMAO.) Dumb niggas don't be loving their lives. They be *wanting* to get hit with the *ytoosie*. The *ytoosie* is when someone tell a person mom that her son had to exchange into the spirit world and she break down screaming, *ytoosie* GOD! He ain't bothered nobody *ytoosie* LORD, *ytoosie* GOD! That's what I mean when I say that these dudes be wanting a nigga to hit them with the ytoosie.

Another weird moment for me was when I was fucking this bad bitch named Renada from Rockingham. She's from where the kid Yomi from. So, this was my bitch. She owned a big ass house in Montibello. She was in love with me, tattooed my name in big letters on her. She said ain't nobody ever fucked her the way I did. Plus, she never had a real nigga until she met me. I could be wherever and see another bitch. I'd tell Renada I wanna fuck *her*. My bitch would go bag the other bitch and let me fuck her right in front of her. That was my bitch, and she was fine as shit too. She had 4 kids, 3 were Mexican and one was Black. She had a daughter named, Risa. I raised this little girl, and I loved her like she was mine. I took her wherever she wanted to go. I took her in the mall and blew racks on her. Whatever she touched, I would buy. I spoiled Risa. She was super pretty, Mexican and Black with long pretty hair. Me and Risa used to hang out all the time. All she used to say was, "No Long, come watch the Bee movie with me."

I watched that movie with Risa every night. When I got home I used to ask Risa if she had any more movies she liked? She would say, "No Long, the Bee movie." Then she would recite the whole movie, doing the acts and all. Me and Risa every night. That was my date. Renada would go to sleep on us.

If y'all ain't know, Trick Daddy ain't the only one that love the kids. Long love the kids.

So, it's me, Renada, and her homegirl, Cassie out of Ellerby, a town near Rockingham. I'm driving them around, we sipping on some liquor. I pulled up in this afterhours spot and backed in. Renada wanted to go in. I declined. This was a dangerous spot. You had to be on point in there. I had been in there plenty of times.

Renada said, "Well, I'm staying in the car with you."

It's about 3 A.M. We just kicking it. So, all of a sudden, a nigga came out the club staggering hard.

Renada hit me and said, "Baby, look at him. He fucked up."

I saw him and said, "Yeah baby, he gone."

The guy glanced up at us, kept walking. I'm not nigga watching, so I turned to the passenger seat to talk to Renada, telling her how pretty she was. Renada looked at Cassie in the backseat and told her I had game. Cassie agreed. All of a sudden I heard,

Boom! Boom!

"Oh shit!" I jumped back and looked. Somebody was knocking on the driver's side window. You know me, I rolled it down. It was the dude that was just staggering.

I spoke, "What's up, homie?"

You wouldn't believe what this motherfucker said next. Mind you, I don't know this motherfucker.

"Aye homeboy, I don't what y'all looking at, but I keep that .40 on deck around here," he said. Then he lifted up his shirt and showed it. Oh, he had a .40 too. Dude was drunk as shit though.

I said, "Oh nah, it ain't no problem, homie." I tried to give him dap. Man, this nigga left my hand hanging.

"Nah homeboy, I'm just letting you know them 40's on deck around here," he reiterated.

This dude introduced me to his .40 too many times for comfort. I was pissed! I told him it wasn't no problem.

As I'm pulling out the parking lot the car was quiet. Out of nowhere Renada hit me in my arm.

"Baby what's wrong with him? Do he know who he talking to?"

That's when Renada saw a side of me she would talk about for the rest of the time we were together. She saw a demon in my eyes as I kicked her and Cassie out of her own car. I went to switch cars and grabbed my real road dog. No clique, my nigga, just me.

Has this motherfucker lost his mind? I'm gonna blow your brains out, boy! I don't fuck around homie. You showed me your gun talking slick? I'm motherfucking Longhead, bitch. Clark Street. I'm gonna kill you, boy and go to your funeral. What you fucking with me for? I'm not fucking with you, pussy!

All I was doing on the way back there was praying, *GOD please let him be there. Please GOD! please.* He asked for this.

Make a long story short, I read in the newspaper the next day that a guy was shot in the chest coming out that same club. Damn, that's fucked up. I hope he made it out alright. A nigga tried to hit him with the ytoosie.

God might be trying to teach these dudes lessons and put them in my path. Man, the world is crazy! Let me find out you do shit on Monday and forget on Thursday. I don't forget. Don't fuck with Mrs. May's grandson, he ain't going for it. All I'm asking is don't make me do it, my nigga. This shit getting wilder and wilder.

You ain't seen nothing yet.

Shout out to Renada and your daughter, Risa. If you are reading this, baby, know I respect you as a

woman and not a little girl. I love you and Risa till death do us part. Risa, I love you baby as if you were my own daughter. I can't wait to hang out with you guys.

Shout out to all the real niggas in the game that go through the real struggles and stand tall. Shout out to all the niggas that play by all the rules. I salute you, my nigga. I'm a real nigga, my nigga. Salute me when you see me, please? I'm begging you, don't jump into my lane. If you do, it better be to wash my car. Anything else is on you. If that's what you looking for, I don't mind giving it to you. I don't know those dudes' names, so I can't give them no shout outs. What I will say is, if you out there getting drunk or whatever, be careful who you approach. You never know what's up with a dude. Even the 48 Laws of Power warn you to Know Who You're Dealing With. Take heed, my niggas. Take heed.

CHAPTER 22
That's Fucked Up

I've seen the worst of the worst. I observe every blessing I received. *I'm from the dirt,* is what, Jay Z said.

Now like I told you, I'm up. I'm well over six figures now. It's only the beginning. I'm going to get that bread. Right now, I'm on chill mode, but please don't jump in my lane. Please, I'm begging you.

You know how it is. I got my flow moving so swift. If you hitting my line its 'cause I know you. Shit's running super sweet or I thought it was. Every time shit running sweet remember what I told you. Shit always happens. It never fails. I know you reading this thinking, '*That Damn Long off the Chain.*' I know the police reading this book too. Sometimes people ain't guilty of everything y'all blame on them. LOL.

Now, I'm riding in Dee's car. She drives a Buick with tinted windows. I told her I wanted to drive the car today. You know she agreed. Anything Dee has, I have, and vice versa; that's' my dog.

So, I'm sitting in front of my grandma's house, hollering at my lil homie Terrence from Bonnie Doone, I had about fifteen-grand on the floor board. I'm in my grandma's yard. We own the property. This is Clark Street, so I'm not thinking anything. Plus, I got my older cousin Trey-Deuce from Campbell Terrace projects on the corner with a bunch of dudes from my hood.

Remember when I used to just watch Clark Street as a kid? Now, not just the street, but the whole hood was mine. I was the one in charge. Grandma always told me to be a leader, not a follower. I was the leader, homie. I followed before, I just followed real niggas.

So, me and Lil T chopping it up. I just threw fifteen-grand on the floor board until I went and got a bag to put the money in. When I looked in the rear-view mirror, the police pulled up. Now this wasn't the regular police, he was an ALE officer, which means he patrolled the liquor stores. He actually lived on Haymount Hill with his wife and kids. Come to find out, they had purchased a bunch of cheap properties around there. (I guess he called himself cleaning up the hood to make the value go up.) (LMAO.) This is our shit. So, when I saw him hop out, I told Lil T this motherfucker was tripping so get out the car. I got out and Lil T got out also. Lil T started walking up Clark Street toward Bergen Street. I walked in my grandma's house and was watching him from the screen door. He started walking in my yard, which is private property. So, he headed for Dee's Buick and I thought about it. I had $15,000 on the floor which was visible. All he had to do was just look in.

I immediately went out and said, "What you doing on my property?" By now, I'm walking toward him to go get my money. This my property, and I hadn't done shit.

Guess what this motherfucker did? He pulled out his gun and said, "Put your hands on your head motherfucker."

I said, "Man, you tripping, homeboy." I put my hands up, but I was talking shit.

He searched me and asked, "Long where the gun at?"

I said, "Man, I ain't got no motherfucking gun. I ain't got shit."

Then he snatched something out of my pocket. Now, I usually don't be slipping but I slipped big this time. It was on some humbug shit, and I forgot I had 2 ounces of crack in my pocket. Shit don't happen to me like this! I don't slip.

I turned around to face him and he started dangling it in the air and said, "Well, what's this?"

I'm from Haymount Hill. You came in my yard, put a gun in my face and dangled my work in my face. So, I did the only thing I knew to do. I'm a real nigga, I tried to reach out and take my shit back. Now, he had a gun in one hand and my dope in the other hand. So, when I reached for it, he was so locked in with holding on to the dope that he snatched way back and stumbled. I saw I had to go all out to get that dope back, so I just took off running. I told you, I run like a deer.

At first, I heard him scream, "Slow down motherfucker or I'ma shoot!" *This motherfucker was so shook he said 'slow down' instead of stop!* I knew he couldn't catch me.

They rode all night looking for me. At least, that is what people told me. I caught a ride on the back street and was at the hotel room chilling. While they were searching for me, I was getting my dick sucked.

So, the next day I found out they towed Dee's car and counted my $15,000 on the hood of the car—before they took that too.

Dee ended up getting $275 from me to get her car out of the impound. The police told her to quit giving her car to drug dealers. (LMAO.) This my bitch! I don't know what they thinking about. She my ryder. When she got her car out of the pound, I found out that I had a warrant for my arrest, so I called my lawyer on his cell. It was a Saturday so me, Dee, her best friend Keshawna, and her boyfriend Tone from Cumberland Road (that's my guy; you know I get love all over) went to the beach to have fun till that Monday, which is the day I told my lawyer I was going to turn myself in. Now mind you, this is the best lawyer in the city so I wasn't worried. We having fun, hanging out all night, having a ball.

So we get back to the room and you know I hit Dee with that boss dick game. I always told Dee that she hooked on this dick, and she would always claim that my dick game was just okay. I can tell by her ways and actions that my dick game is serious though.

When we woke up on Sunday morning I had a lot of missed calls from my lil' cuz. I knew something wasn't right, so I hit him back.

"Boy, the police kicked in Grandma's door last night looking for you," he immediately informed me.

I was pissed! Those motherfuckers knew I didn't live with my grandma. At this time, she was 74 years old.

He continued, "Yeah, they dragged her out of her bed, handcuffed her, busted the windows out of her house and ransacked the place. They cussed her and Aunt Boogie out too."

Now I'm super pissed! "It ain't nothing in that house," I said. I had Mo's house and plenty of hoes for that. They knew nothing was in that house. They was just so fed up with my shit and wanted to get my attention. Trust me, they had it now.

I called my lawyer instantly and told him I was on my way back. I wanted him to go with me to turn myself in that day. I called my lawyer and told him I didn't care if my bond was half-a-million dollars, I wanted him to bond me out. He agreed and I called him when I was on my way downtown with my lawyer. I was fresh to death in a pair of Dolce shades that cost $650.

So, while we're in the precinct, waiting for the officer to come and serve the warrant, guess who showed up with the officer? The ALE officer that started everything. He held a pad and pen in his hand while I was sitting beside my lawyer looking straight ahead. This motherfucker tried to rattle me.

"Why you turn yourself in? You usually run," he said. "What have you been doing, shooting people? Is everybody still scared of you?"

While he's talking, me and my lawyer are just staring straight ahead waiting to see the magistrate.

Frustrated, he snapped, "Motherfucker, you think you slick? We will get you!"

For the first time, I spoke, "Officer, do you have the time?" My lawyer looked at his watch and told me it was around 7 p.m. I looked back at the officer and said, "Do you mind if I get something to drink?"

My lawyer walked me to the water fountain and when we returned to the table I said, "Officer, do you mind, if you got everything off your chest, I need speak to my lawyer for a second."

He stood from the table and said, "Fuck you!"

My bond was set at $5,000. It only cost me $500 to get out. I don't know if it was because the magistrate had saw my grandmother on the news. See, my family was so pissed about what they had done to my grandmother's house that they called the news station to come to the house and record it. (If you have YouTube, type in *'Police vandalize 74-year-old woman's house.'*) The NAACP wanted to pursue charges with a lawsuit, but my grandmother declined. When the public demanded answers, the police claimed they went in with force because I was considered violent. Mind you, I hadn't been found guilty of shit.

Anyway, I'm out on bond again. One day, the ALE officer was cruising through the block. He realized that he got lucky catching me with something that day. So, I'm sitting on my grandma's front porch and she was standing in the screen door talking to me. Mind you, I'm still pissed about the way they did her and her house. So, it's just me and her, and he stopped in front of my house.

He said, "Come over here, Long." I acted like I didn't hear him.

My grandma said, "Boy, come in the house."

I said, "Grandma, I ain't doing nothing. He ain't going to run me in the house."

So he said something else and I flipped out. It was the first time I ever cussed in front of my grandma.

I stood up and pointed, "Don't your kids live right there, motherfucker?" I yelled. "The kids you love?"

Oh, he understood what I said loud and clear. He threw his car in park and jumped out.

"What's that supposed to mean, you punk? You threatening my kids?"

My grandma got mad because she know I got issues. She said, "Look police officer, go on about your business. This boy ain't bothering you. Leave him alone."

He jumped in the car and pulled off. A couple of days later, him and his wife moved out of that house. *Good, get the fuck out!*

Meanwhile, life went on. I still had a case over my head and my lawyer was charging me $15,000 to handle it. He came to me and said he got me a deal. I wouldn't have to go to prison, just a felony on my record and probation. If I violated the probation, I would have to do 6-8 months.

I looked that lawyer in his eyes and said, "Man, I don't need no felony on my record. What if I bring you $10,000 more? Can you get it to a misdemeanor?" He told me he would see.

By the time I made it to the Hill, he called me back. My plea was for $25,000 he turned 2 ounces of crack into a misdemeanor. He took 2 ounces of crack and made it seem as if I had some Ziploc baggies. (LMAO! Money talks! Get your bread up, lil' nigga.) I still had to do 45 days for the drug paraphernalia. They had to get something out of me.

When I came home, I came home on unmonitored probation. If I violated I would do 45 more days. I was cool with it as long as I didn't get a felony.

I lost $15,000 and spent $25,000 on my legal troubles. I was at a $40,000 loss. Here I was, heading back to the County Jail *again.* This time for a 45-day misdemeanor. This shit keeps going and going.

I was smiling this time, but you ain't seen shit yet. It felt like these police and niggas were plotting on me, homie. I was legendary at this time! They were out to get me—I could feel it...

Shout out to my grandmother. Once again, you the strongest woman I ever met in my life. It hurts me to know I put you through all of this at your age, but you Ford tough. You always told me, "Never let the left hand know what the right hand is doing."

There is nothing in the world I wouldn't do for you. You always call me your youngest son. So, mom, I know I didn't go the road you wanted me to go, but one thing is for sure, you didn't raise no punk.

I had a guy run up on me and say, "Man, we crazy, but we do drugs. You don't do no drugs, Long, and you the crazy one."

I replied with the 2Pac definition of Thug Life: The Hate U Gave Little Infants Fuck Everybody. My anger is fucked by a troubling childhood, and this woman was the only one there. That's why she's the only one who can really contain the beast inside.

You think you heard it all? You haven't heard the half of it yet. Keep reading...

Police forcefully enter grandmother's home

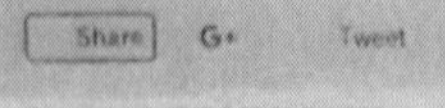

September 7, 2009 6:56:22 PM PDT

By Gilbert Baez

FAYETTEVILLE -- A 74-year-old grandmother told Eyewitness News police used excessive force while executing a search warrant at her home.Bessie Small said a small army of officers snatched her out of bed Sunday night, held a gun to her head and ransacked her house.

"I was sleeping and I heard something ? and they ran (in) and when I woke up they said don't move," Small said. "(They) grabbed me out by my arm ? my arm is still sore, and had broke the fan and drug me over the fan and put their knee ? their foot in my back."

She said officers also smashed in her big screen TV and damaged her property for no apparent reason.

"This chair ? was turned around the other way and they smashed my head in this chair and told me not to move," Small said. "They had guns out ? they were cursing at me calling me talking about we ought to kill you old woman." The officers were looking for one of her grandsons who hasn't lived with her in two years.

Small's grandson, 24-year-old Larry Everett, recently had murder charges against him dropped and is now wanted on drug related charges.

Authorities said he has a history of violence and he was recently seen leaving Small's house, which is also his last known address.

"They say they were looking for my grandson," Small said. "And I told them ? 'y'all can ask anybody, cause I've been here 30 years and people all around here know I live here by myself'."

A police spokesperson was not available to talk on camera Monday, but the desk sergeant told Eyewitness News that it was a legally executed search warrant and they can be violent and destructive.

Small said she plans to file a complaint against the department.

My Beautiful Grandmother Ms. May

CHAPTER 23
Grandma I Got That Bag

I sat in jail for 38 days. I already knew all the C.O.'s down there so I had it sweet. Dudes in jail was amazed being on the block with me. I remember sitting in my cell thinking, *This shit is wild! They respect a nigga to the fullest.* Then I looked in the mirror and said, *Oh they better.*

There were young guys in there staring and amazed. They were like, "You Long from Haymount Hill? We heard so much about you, homie. You a real nigga and we respect you, Big Homie."

I'm talking 'bout dudes telling me they would do anything for me. Little did they know, they don't call me Long for nothing. I didn't get nobody to do anything for Long. I'm hands-on. I don't care how much money I get. That's just me. You know the saying, if you want something done right, you gotta do it yourself? I live by that, homie.

So, when I'm on the way out of jail on my 38th day, I had a limo out front. Now, a limo out front was major only because of who I am. The guards found out the limo was waiting on me out there at 8 a.m. when I was supposed to be released and took their time with letting me go. So, I called my people and told them to call the limo company and tell the driver not to move that limo—even if it's late night when they let me go.

They finally let me out and a thick canteen lady came to get me. It was around one in the afternoon.

The canteen lady said, "Everett, what you doing with a Limo outside?"

I knew all the guards were talking about it. They all knew me.

So I said, "Look, shorty, get me out of jail. I was gonna have my Maserati out front, but I decided against it."

She blushed, she was game. Little did she know, I was trying to get back to the money. Fuck her.

You wouldn't believe who got out the same day I did. Motherfucking Kojack! He was being released from the country on some bullshit charges.

As soon as we saw each other Kojack said, "Nephew, what's up? Boy, Unc fucked up; you need to throw a dog a bone."

I was so excited about getting out. I told Kojack, "Man, come on Unc. I got a limo out front. Let's just get out of here."

We got out front and hopped in the limo. Now what I had placed in the back of the limo was $20,000, 3 brand-new phones, and a big bottle of Grey Goose. Me and Unc sat in the back, rode the city, and got drunk.

Now, me and Unc ain't been this close in a long time. So, he saw me sitting in that limo with twenty grand in my lap, making all these major phone calls, and had to give me my props.

Unc said, "Nephew, you got the game. You came a long way."

I didn't let Unc know it, but to hear my mentor/rival/uncle saying this made me feel good like a motherfucker.

I took Kojack shopping with me. I got us some sunglasses, two pair of shades for $1,500.

Unc said, "Fuck these shades!"

I told Unc that shit ain't 'bout nothing. We hit up some stores and got fresh, then we hopped back in the limo. I got dropped off to take a shower and told the limo driver to take Kojack wherever he needed to go as long as he was back to pick us up for the club tonight. It was Friday night so when I got ready, I wanted to ride solo and get my thoughts together.

I had left my Maserati in Renada's garage at our house. When I lifted the garage and hopped in that motherfucker, I had that Jay-Z booming. As I sipped my liquor and pushed my Maserati, I looked in the mirror like, *Man, you a hell of a dude.* I even repeated what Mo had said so many times. I even heard the words in his voice: *'When it comes to this game, Long, you a playing motherfucker!'* I'm Longhead from Haymount Hill. I'm a Jack Boy's idol, a hustler's motivation, and a bad bitch's dream guy.

While I'm riding around, so many people looking into my car. Girls smiling, showing the thirst. I really bypassed them. I went to my other crib and grabbed all my jewelry. $98,000 worth, to be exact, but I just say $100,000. Am I wrong? I have black diamonds *and* blue diamonds. I have a name plate with *Long* spelled out in different colored diamonds.

To all who haven't read in my story, did you see where I came from? You saw what I been through? You saw what I been putting down. What makes my story different is I'm not a sucker with money. I'm a real nigga with money.

So, I got on all my jewelry riding out in my Maserati. I hit this lil bitch I was fucking, this McNeil girl. She was in love with me. I slid through and got some of that good head. She's the only black girl I ever got head from that didn't have a gag reflex. I ended up fucking a few of her family members. They good people.

When I say I got my dick sucked on every corner, it was no lie. I already had a lot of hoes before all this big-boy shit. Now when I wake up, I got girls texting me, asking if I want my dick sucked before I get my day started. They call themselves my personal dick suckers. I couldn't make this shit up if I wanted to. I'm only telling you my life. I knew I had the ball in my hand and they all respected me because they knew I still didn't play no bullshit.

Me, Kojack, and a few more people went to the club that night we got out. "V.I.P." We threw bundles of money in that motherfucker.

The funniest shit I ever did in that same club was turn the waitress into a stripper while I loaded her with money. She called me the next day and told me she got fired. I guess she thought I was gonna take care of her. I did fuck her one time since she got fired for fucking with me, but she was on her own.

I had so many threesomes and orgies with girls. I had bitches that would call me over a house full of girls, and I'd be fucking all of them while they eating pussy. Shit, I ran so many trains on hoes, to tell you the truth, I don't give a fuck about a bitch. However, I learn to love her when she loyal to me. I don't care what she do with her pussy, I can't control that. I'm gonna wear a condom anyway.

I was balling so hard and on top like a motherfucker. I can't lie, I always been up but never like this. I was already known heavy, my new weight ain't do nothing but add on. I even fucked two sisters at the same time. Naw, y'all didn't hear me... I was fucking one sister and when I saw her at the club, I told her the only way she was going with me tonight was to bring her sister.

She said, "Damn Long, you make me sick. You wanna fuck everyone!" Fifteen minutes later, she came dragging her sister and said, "She's down. We ready."

This shit was wild!

I ran through all the girl cliques. I watched them snake each other. Best friends, cousins, and all. I've seen two cousins eat each other pussy right in front of me, then bring in their best friend and make her help them suck my dick. I'm trying to give you all the most exciting stories of how that money make them do. But you got to wear condoms.

I was fucking this girl and was chilling. I told her to call her cousin because she's fine and I wanted her to suck my dick while she watched. She did. When the girl got there, she thought she was just coming to see her cousin.

Her cousin told her, "I called you over here to suck Long's dick."

Now this bitch was pretty. She said, "No girl, I'm married. I can't do that."

Then my bitch said these words: "Bitch, I ain't gonna be mad. You know you wanna fuck Long anyway. All I told you about him. You know that dick game good, and he ain't gonna say nothing."

The girl started sucking my dick. She must have forgotten about her husband. Her cousin kept telling her to suck my dick. Then she asked me if she was doing it right.

I told her the truth, "Her head better than yours baby, but I love you, bitch."

She looked me in the eyes and said, "Nut in her mouth."

Her cousin pulled up and said, "He can't nut in my mouth."

My bitch looked at her and said, "Bitch, keep sucking."

I bust all in her pretty little mouth.

Enough of them hoes. You get the picture I'm painting. This shit was wild. I didn't put a name on these girls. I vowed to protect their privacy. Besides, I don't kiss and tell, so back to this balling shit.

I was pushing a BMW 650 drop-top. Mo was with me when I handed the car dealer $50,000 cash and drove it off the lot.

Mo said, "Aye yo, my nigga, this that shit doctors and lawyers drive. You putting this shit down!"

Now, let me stop the book for a second. Man, I'm little Larry who nobody wanted, who told you when they threw me to the wolves, I came back leading the pack. This shit for real for real. 745's Audis and shit... ballin is my future. I'm spending anywhere from a 100 to 150 grand on the re-up twice a month. At *least* that, sometimes. That's 300K a month on the re-up. I'm living in top-notch condos with elevators in the complex. Staying in big-boy cribs, in-ground pools in the backyard. Apartments everywhere. Longhead from Clark Street. I even went to Winston Salem and offered some girls two grand if they could find Erika for me, but they basically said, *fuck Erika what about us.* I don't blame them I looked like money.

One time I was in Greensboro at a club pushing my Maserati. It's in VIP. I left it running while I partied. I'm in this bitch, dolo, with all my jewelry on. Now here comes trouble... Some young niggas came and stood right in front of me and beside me. I knew what they was thinking, but I was thinking too. I was saying, *please don't do it.* I had this bad bitch with me named Leann from Greensboro. She did hair down there off High Point Road. I sent her to buy us two drinks. When she got back, I whispered in her ear. Now I'm a jack boy so I can see them from a mile away. I'm just so sophisticated and you still stuck in position.

I whispered in Leann's ear, "Don't look now, but I need to know, do you know them dudes right there and how to get up with them?"

After she played it cool, she looked at them and whispered back, "Them two boys there be robbing people. That other boy is they cousin. I do one of their baby mama's hair, and I know where his mama stays."

(I told you they was jack boys.)

I looked at her and said, "Are you sure?"

She said, "Yes Darrell, I'm positive."

When she said that, I turned up. I'm dolo, my nigga, with big-boy jewelry on, out of town. I had about 30 grand on me. I started pulling money out, knot after knot. I'm taunting these niggas... *I dare you to touch my chain or take this money! You gonna wish you didn't.*

Leann said, "Darrell, why you keep pulling out all that money?"

I spoke, "Because I can, shorty."

I'm looking like a chandelier in this motherfucker. I dared them to jump and I got the rundown on them. How you gone rob the robber? This shit you looking at might be another nigga shit I took. You think you gonna take from Longhead? No matter where I'm at, I'm HIM. Boy, stop!

Anyways, these lil' niggas was smarter than they looked. I guess they could sense I was a gangsta in this motherfucker, dolo and cocky. I know what I'm gonna do when it's time, no breaks, all go-mode.

I saw them in the parking lot and they kept it moving. Smart move lil' niggas. I'm not your average baller; this shit ain't worth the ytoosie. That's what you gone get for fucking with my chain.

I knew shit was real when I started counting money with a money machine. I used to let niggas owe me 40 and 50 grand. That's more money than you seen at once. Like I told you, I wasn't the richest nigga to come through my city, but I was the most popular and they knew they couldn't fuck with me.

See, it's like I said, them getting money niggas only did one thing. They got money and that's all they did. Outside of that, they was soft. Not me though. You can catch me in the jack boy's spot late night on their side of town with all my jewelry on. I'm gonna front them that work and they gonna pay me. You can't even wear all your jewelry on their side of town and get caught slipping. They gonna take all your shit. Me? I'm in their hoods late night, gambling with the grimiest of the grimy and they know not to play with me. Not only can I hang with the jack boys, they look up to me and they respect me. I can pull up on the shooters and they gonna look up to me and respect me. I can hang out with the ballers and they gonna respect me and fear me all at the same time. You could never do what I do. You only talented in one area. I'm multi-talented motherfuckers. I'm Longhead bitch from Haymount Hill. Don't make me, and I just might not cut the fuck up.

So, all the niggas that was getting more money than me, I gave you your props and told the truth. I also told the truth when I said with all your money, you couldn't do what I did. You was ducking and hiding with all yours. I was front row with mine, and I never paid a nigga to do my dirty work. I handled all that myself. I'm a hands-on motherfucker. Why you think they respect me? Because I'm gonna be the one beside your house with mosquito and ant spray on me because them motherfuckers be worrisome when you got to wait patiently for your target. (LMAO.)

Let me stop, I don't know nothing about that. I'm only Little Larry from Haymount Hill, Mrs. May's grandson. I ain't like that. Just please, don't jump in my lane, homie.

Shout out to the young niggas that look up to me. I respect you, lil homie. Follow the rules, no matter what they do. Do you! When you see me ballin' out of control and doing my thing, know as much as I've learned and know, I didn't get it over night, my nigga. It took years of experience—lots of it—to make it to this level. You gotta live and make it out. I doubt you'll ever put it down like I did. Not saying you can't but you gotta be a hell of a nigga.

Now, think of who taught you this shit. Now what's their outcome of the game? Were they real niggas in the end? If they wasn't, then disregard all their teachings and get the right guidance, homie. Keep your head up. Know it gets rough, but you gotta hold on and be strong. Only real niggas survive the struggle.

I love you lil' niggas that's coming after me. Put that shit down, my nigga.

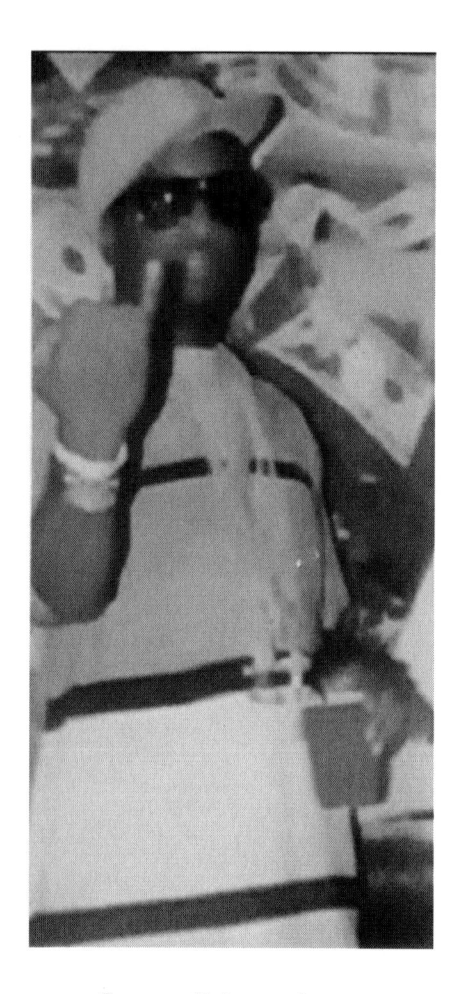

Long all bossed up.

CHAPTER 24
I Can't Believe This Shit

Now this shit moving too sweet. Anything I want is at my fingertips. From all the bad bitches to driving my dream car. I'm from the slums, my nigga. The real slums. Niggas go their whole life in the game and don't reach this level, specifically playing as hard as I'm playing. I'm *really* in the streets, every night, every single day, hands-on. The only thing I stopped doing is serving. The only way I'm serving you is if you locked in with me and I know your whereabouts every second of the day.

I'm going so hard my homies fucking bad bitches off my name. Because they hanging with me, these bitches wanna be in the circle. What can I say? It was my turn, and I fucking deserved it because I'm a real nigga, homie.

So, like I've been telling you through this whole book, when shit going too sweet, you already know.

By now, Koo-Koo was rolling. She would pull up and get oz's, pull off, and wouldn't pay for them. Why would she, when her son that she left for dead is ballin'? I wouldn't even trip on KooKoo. She was like a distant sister or something. I'm hitting KooKoo off. She would move it and pay me sometimes. Other times she'd say, fuck me. This is KooKoo though. She still pushed me out that ass of hers, but everything I learned, I learned on my own by paying attention. No mother nor father can take credit for my accomplishments, only my grandmother, Mo, and the streets. KooKoo was alright. She was down by law; everyone knew her. She had been in the streets her whole life, so KooKoo was KooKoo.

One day KooKoo was at this liquor house she visited often. She met a guy over there at the liquor house, and him and KooKoo was kicking it. (If you asking me, I think the Dude was fucking KooKoo, but I don't know for sure. I never asked her about her sex life.) The dude got real cool with KooKoo, so he coming around there hanging out. He end up being a drug dealer. He was older, so he was buying 8-balls and quarters from KooKoo. She had that already on deck and they kicking it tough. They became close, but KooKoo got her work from me and did her own thing at this time.

So, one day I'm at my bitch Renada's house sleeping. We go to sleep late. If I'm not watching the Bee movie with Risa, I'll be watching movies with Renada. Then, at 7 a.m. I'll drop the kids off at school and take Risa to get McDonalds. Then I would come back home, turn on the Bee movie for Risa so she could watch it and eat her food. This was an everyday schedule. So I woke up after 2:30 p.m. to pick the kids up from school. They have to be picked up by 3:30 p.m. I was a family man, we had a routine over here. I'm going hard still, just smoother. So, when I woke up there was 24 missed calls from KooKoo. I thought something was wrong.

I called her back first. I had 67 missed calls but she got the call first. Everybody else could wait. Renada was cooking me breakfast like she did whenever I woke up, even if it was in the afternoon.

So KooKoo picked up and said, "Boy I had a play for a O.Z. and you didn't pick up. So, I kept it in the family and took him to Jig."

I said, "KooKoo, you mean to tell me you blew my phone up for one ounce? I don't care about that. Even if I would have woke up, I wouldn't have came out for that unless I was in the hood.

So, I said, "Ok KooKoo, that's cool. Is that all you wanted? I'm 'bout to go."

Then she said, real slick like, "I know you a Big Baller now, you don't got time for the little people. I still gotta eat."

I said, "Ok KooKoo."

I forgot to mention how KooKoo got a real slick mouth so she gonna talk crazy. So, I went about my day like I always did. I kept the same routine.

Hold up, let me help the thugs out for a second. When you find a routine that works for you, keep it. Don't change it up. You feel me? That's what I was doing.

See, I bred jealousy and envy in a whole different way then the average person did. They knew they couldn't rob me or take nothing from me, mean-mug me, say nothing crazy to me, or try to play me in any kind of way. So, they had to keep everything on the low and bite their tongue. They're smarter than they look is all I can say.

So, one day I'm chilling like I do, and I got a call from a private number. I answered. It was a jail house call from Jig. So, you know me, I'm on joke time when I accepted. Jig is like me. He moves smart, and he never been convicted of a felony either.

I said, "Hello Bitch, what the fuck you doing down there, drunk driving or driving on them revoked license?" I'm laughing the whole time.

Then my brother said, "Man, right now ain't the time to joke, homie. Come get me, shit is real."

By the tone of his voice I knew something wasn't right. Jig has been my best friend for years. I know dude better than myself. So, I got serious real quick. Jokes went out the window.

I said, "Ok bruh, I'm coming to get you. I'ma send me bondsman there right now. What your bond so I can tell him?"

He said, "It's a quarter-million."

In shock, I said, "Bitch, what the fuck you do?"

He said, "Seriously, come get me, bruh. Shit real."

I said, "Ok homie."

Jig made bond the next day. When he got out he called me so I could come talk to him. That's when he ran me this story right here.

"Man Long, that dude was the police."

I said, "What dude homie, the dude KooKoo brought to me? I don't know what you talking 'bout."

He said, "One day KooKoo called me from this dude's phone because she said hers went dead trying to call you. She called me and came to my house to buy an ounce. She broke off an 8-Ball from the dude shit while she was in my house."

That sounded like KooKoo (always scamming.)

Jig continued, "So, she took it outside and they pulled off. I get a call back from the dude, this time from the same phone KooKoo called me from. He said, man I know you don't know me, but I ain't dealing with that bitch anymore. She stole some of my work."

So being that KooKoo brought the dude, Jig's guard was down because he knew KooKoo wouldn't bring no harm to him. So, Jig told him not to worry about that, he'd straighten that out. Just hit him up and he was gonna clean up KooKoo's mess. When the dude called back and got two ounces, Jig added a quarter on top for the mishaps and they went from there. (You know, I'm with Jig damn near every day. Can you believe I wasn't with him not one time when he served this dude? God loves me, homie!)

So, the dude started buying ounces of crack left and right. He had bought 12 ounces all together. The last time he ordered 2 ounces Jig said when he got there he asked the dude where the fuck he was moving this shit.

The man said, "Oh, I drop it off at the liquor houses and go back and pick up my money."

Jig said when he told him that he knew he was the police. He told the dude he would call him back because he forgot to bring them. Jig explained to me that he was trying to get away from this police motherfucker. Well, what Jig didn't know is that he was wired and the police in the parking lot heard the whole conversation. They bum rushed the car, shot the flash bangs and knocked him off with the 2 ounces of crack he brought for the dude.

After hearing this, I'm at a loss for words, and I'm super pissed. I told Jig let's go over KooKoo house right now.

Jig said, "That's not all."

I asked, "What's up?"

Jig said, "When I got downtown, they told me, 'We want Longhead; this wasn't meant for you. We will make all this disappear if you give him up. You the only one who can get close to him.'"

Jig said they damn near begged him to set me up. Thirsty motherfuckers! I'm surrounded by solid motherfuckers. What the fuck they thinking?

Jig said he told them to take him to his cell.

They asked Jig, "What, you scared of him too? Do you know anything about any shootings or murders? We know that's his dope you're selling. What you don't understand is this whole sting was for him."

So they sent the police to get *in* with my momma because they saw a way in through her. But they missed me. Thank God for me taking the time to watch The Bee movie with Risa. (LMAO.) I thank GOD for that Bee movie.

So, before they took Jig to his cell, two guys came in and introduced themselves as the Feds. They told Jig, "We want Longhead off the streets. If you don't help us, your case will go Federal. I can bet you this is your first and last offer."

Again, Jig told them to take him to his cell.

They said, "Ok smart ass, you're going to get a shitload of time in a federal prison."

When he told me the rest of the story I knew I was *hot* because I was into too much shit. They felt like I got away with too much shit. I heard stories of how the police wanted me bad, but they hit close to home with this one.

Now it was time to go by and visit KooKoo, because she fucked up big-time. We grabbed a bottle of liquor and headed to KooKoo's house.

When we pulled up I told Jig not to say anything. I wanted to talk to her first. We grabbed the liquor and walked to KooKoo's door off Pilot Street and knocked. She answered and said, "There goes my boys."

I walked past her and sat on the couch. Jig was on the other couch she was talking to KooKoo, and I was trying to figure out how to approach this.

I told KooKoo, "Sit down and let me ask you something."

She sat down and said, "What's wrong?"

I said, "You know the man you turned on to Jig. Where is he from? Where does he live?"

She said, "I didn't turn anyone on to Jig. What are you talking about?"

"The guy that you purchased the ounce for when you tried calling my phone," I reminded her.

She said, "Oh." Then she came out with everything.

She knew about the guy. She met him at the liquor house and she didn't knew where he lived.

"Why you asking for?" KooKoo asked.

I said, "Because you let a snake into something that has been running smooth for us."

She said, "What you mean?"

I came out with it. "That fucking man is the police! Jig just got out on a quarter-million-dollar bond and I'm trying to figure out why you brought him around us."

She gasped for air, "Oh my gosh, Larry. No, no, please Larry, he ain't the police."

"Ain't no need to say that now 'cause the Feds is coming in."

She said, "Oh no, Larry, I just met him at the liquor house."

I said, "Why would you bring a guy you met at the liquor house to us? Have you lost your mind? If you served him then you got charges too," I pointed out. "How many times you serve him?"

In a panic, she answered, "I served him a couple of 8-Balls and some quarters. He always wanted to meet you and deal with you, Larry, but I told him my son wasn't going to meet or deal with him."

"So ma, you telling me you didn't think nothing when he wanted to meet me?"

She said, "No son."

I said, "What are you gonna do 'cause you got charges coming, I'm pretty sure."

Jig ran down to her what he told me. The next thing I knew, KooKoo called a ride and got the hell out of dodge. She said, fuck that, she wasn't going down there—until the same U.S. Marshals that tracked me down came to my sister's house looking for her. They asked my sister how I was doing and told her to relay the message to me that since I was hiding my mother out, they might have to track me down.

I took KooKoo down there with a lawyer and bonded ole' KooKoo out. My mama and my best friend had some heavy charges, and even though my momma didn't serve him a lot, they charged KooKoo with Conspiracy also every time Jig served him. So, KooKoo and Jig were co-defendants, and the whole sting was to get me. This shit was wild! My best friend and my mama.

So, me and Jig partying hard because we know they 'bout to come pick him up. One night we leaving the club in one of those new Chargers. Jig brought this young boy with us and he wanted to drive. Jig told me to let him drive since he had license. So, I let him drive, while I got in the backseat. Jig was on the passenger side, and he was hollering at some hoes at the store on Bragg Boulevard right beside the Palace. A bitch I was fucking pulled up in my Tahoe with Jig's bitch riding with her. They pulled up on some bullshit, so I got in the backseat and Jig jumped in. I told them hoes to give us a second, let us shake them and we was gonna call.

The young boy pulled off driving and Jig's bitch and my bitch hopped in our ass following us. Now, they in my Tahoe that I gave the ungrateful bitch. So, I told the young boy to lose them. Jig told the young boy to lose them so we can get up with the other hoes. He gunned the Charger, and eventually lost them, but he kept driving fast. Jig warned him to slow down because there was a curve coming up. Before we knew it, the car did twenty flips. When it stopped, I was dazed. I regained my consciousness and busted the window out to escape out the car. When I came out the car, I saw my dawg off Haymount Hill. He knew it was us flipping in the car. He had watched us flipping and came over there. This other lady was on the phone with the police. She saw the accident and stopped too.

My dawg had been at the club with us. He said, "Where's Jig? He ain't in the car."

We went searching for Jig and found him in the woods in front of a tree with his head busted from where the tree had stopped him. He was unresponsive. I could hear the police sirens coming. They were getting close. I told my dawg to stay with bruh 'cause I had to get out of there and get ghost.

Jig died for a long time and they brought him back. (I like to say God brought him back.) I wanted to Ytoosie that young boy! Fucking clown, about to take out two real niggas on some dumb shit. Jig was in a coma for a long time. The doctor told his mom to pull the plug. He was gonna be a vegetable if he woke up.

When I went over there she told me, "Lil Larry, over my dead body is the only way I'm pulling that plug."

I was sick seeing my best friend laid up like this.

Then one day I'm on the block chilling. Jig's bitch, MeMe, brought her drunk ass out there and walked up on me screaming and shit.

"I hate you! Don't nothing ever happen to you! You do all this shit out here motherfucker and don't nothing ever happen to you. It's always bad shit happening to everybody around you!"

I'd had enough. I said, "You drunk bitch! Get away from me before I fuck you up."

She said, "What you gonna do? Kill me? Huh, Longhead, you gonna kill me?"

If this wasn't Jig's bitch, I would have spit in this bitch's face I don't play that shit coming from a nigga or a bitch.

I told them niggas, "Get this bitch away from me."

They walked her away but she yelled louder and louder, so I got ghost on that drunk bitch.

Jig woke up about a year later. Man, I was happy and thanking God! I promise you I was. When he came through, he was legally blind, so he can't see.

Right after he regained consciousness, the Feds kept their word and still picked him up. My dawg kept it "G," blind and all. He didn't tell shit. My motherfucking nigga! The judge gave him a downward departure because of his blind situation and bruh went up the road.

I paid a top-notch lawyer for KooKoo because her shit was State. The Feds didn't want her, I guess. So, the lawyer I hired for her got her 5 years' probation since she didn't have a record.

This shit was getting wild as a motherfucker. If you only knew what a nigga went through. And that was just the beginning. Shit was about to take another twist. Wait till you see what happens next.

Shout out to my motherfucking brother, Jig. I know somebody got to read this to you, but I want you to know I love you, my nigga. Like Mo used to tell us, we graveyard niggas. My nigga, that means we taking this shit to the graveyard, my nigga. You one of the realest niggas I ever met in my life. They still trying to put it down like us, but they can't. We can't be duplicated, my nigga. Tell your mom, Ms. Kat, I love her. And to your lil' brother, Bun Bun, that caught the body at 17 years old, doing 20 years on State... hold your head, Bun Bun.

Aye Jig, on my soul, nigga there ain't nothing I wouldn't do for you, and you already know that. I can't wait to reunite with you. From your little brother, Long.

My best friend Jig

CHAPTER 25
This Lil' Nigga

So shit, at this point in my life I'm up and winning. I can't lose. My decision making skills are up to par. I'm making healthy choices, but shit still haywire.

Then I'll be damned, all of a sudden some more bullshit hit the fan. You remember Tone, Keshawna's boyfriend? Well, he let his three homies, White Boy Mike, Rell, and Rodriguez borrow his red Dodge Magnum one night. One of his homies, Rodriguez, had just survived a bullet to the head. If you ask me he shouldn't have been nowhere near the streets because the bullet caused him to move slowly. Anyways, somebody pulled up on the Magnum with an AK-47 and let it go. White Boy Mike got hit, but was able to get away. Rell and Rodriguez got hit up and died on the scene. So now the homicide detectives got two bodies on their hands. Tone my man, I fucked with him and Rodriguez, but the Homicide detectives showed up at my grandmother's house saying I killed them two dudes because Tone owed me a bunch of money. I told you, every time bodies drop and they don't know who did it, they suspect me. I don't know why. These motherfuckers crazy. Even though I had nothing to do with that shit, I had to add it to my collection of things they blamed on me. Rell and Rodriquez's murders are still unsolved to this day.

In my hood I'm just going hard, ducking the bullshit that comes with this shit, right? So there was this lil' nigga named T-Black. A young kid that stayed on the other side of Haymount Hill by Robeson Street park. I used to see him on the block a lot so I started taking notes and watching him. He buying my work from my homie that's serving the whole hood.

One day I asked my homie, "What's up with T-Black? He on it, ain't he?"

Well I found out he be buying 8-Balls and quarters all during the day, and he be out pulling all-nighters by himself. I can't lie, I was curious. I like young niggas that got money on the mind.

One day I'm riding through the hood and I see this lil' nigga standing in the same spot where Metro was killed. I had to get him off that block and bring him a part of the winning team, so I told my homie to give him an ounce and see how he does. He did right, so I stepped it up on him. Before you knew it, T-Black was moving a half of brick every other day with one of my phones. He hustling all night, but except for standing on a block he hustling from behind a wheel now. I grew to love this lil' nigga and I considered him my lil' brother.

I stepped everything up about him.

I changed his whole life around, The hoes fucking him. They know he up-and-coming. Everybody knows he rocking with me. He in the club looking like a mini Long with top-notch designer shades, hat to the back, fresh to death, blowing money fast.

I'm gonna tell you like I tell anybody who ask me about T-Black, he got some knowledge. How do I know? I gave it to him. I drilled it into him. I told you, can't nobody be beside me and be dumb because they might crash and crash me with them. So, if I got you close to me, I got to teach you. I'll admit though, I forgot to teach him one thing about the jealous chatter.

I can recall times I pulled up and hoes might say, "Where your do-boy at?"

I'd put them in their place fast, but what I didn't know is T-Black couldn't handle this kind of talk. It got to him, his pride maybe. It's my fault, I should have warned him the talk was coming. Personally, I didn't see the big deal. I didn't have a problem being called a do-boy for real niggas when I was young. I knew my position, and like I said, in exchange for my services I got A-1 game that got me in the position I was in. T-Black couldn't see it that way. He thought that was belittlement. Another thing that threw T-Black off is he heard all this shit about me growing up and he couldn't figure me out. They say I'm this ruthless motherfucker but when I'm around I'm always giving knowledge on how to outthink the police, putting money up, and just life lessons in general. T- Black was still young so his eyes haven't seen enough. He wanted me to fulfill his eyesight with the stories he heard. What T-Black didn't know is you can be around me all day and you still can't figure me out. It comes from being at the top of your game.

Well anyway, I guess ole' T-Black thought Longhead got soft and washed up and all he did was get money now. Unfortunately, he was 30% right and 70% wrong. I'm from the heart of the streets. Before anybody play me, we going all out.

T-Black broke my heart. I loved him like a brother and he reminded me of my lil brother, Metro. T-Black stopped answering my phone calls and he distanced himself all the way from me. So I let him go.

One day I'm backed in at my sis Mek Mek's yard sitting in a rental car. A kid named Carter pulled up and asked to hop in. Now Carter used to be a hell of a football player. He was destined to go pro. He traded it in for the streets, but that's his story, I'm telling mine. All I know is this is the message that Carter brought to me.

"Long, man, T-Black and Wayne talking about breaking in a girl's house where you keep a lot of pounds," Carter said. "T-Black told me and Wayne this last night, so Wayne down. I played like I was down, but I ain't crazy."

I said, "Damn, why you telling me? Why you ain't down with robbing Longhead?"

Carter stated, "Are you crazy? You ain't about to kill me, I ain't stupid! I don't know what the fuck wrong with them niggas."

So, I told Carter to link up with them tonight and continue the conversation, but this time record it with his phone. He agreed and bounced.

So, while I'm sitting in the car heartbroken, I smiled to myself. "Damn, lil homie want my spot and he don't even know what I been through to get here," I said aloud. "He probably would have been gone crazy."

The next day Carter called me and we met up outside the hood. He hopped in and looked around my car.

"Damn, you was just driving a different car yesterday," he noted. "But here is the recorder."

He put the phone on the middle part and hit play. This is what I heard from T-Black's voice:

"Man, Long is a smart motherfucker. He only goes to this house once a week or once every two weeks. The pounds up high in the attic—Mo taught him that. But we can't go straight to the stash because he gone know I did it and he gonna kill me. So we gotta tear up the house first..."

When it stopped I took my phone and recorded it. Then I turned it into my ringtone. I told Carter if they wanna break in the house, egg them on. I'm going out of town this weekend so try to get them to kick the door in.

Well, on that night I was in the house waiting. Carter kept texting me, saying they wanted him to kick the door in and T-Black was acting like he wasn't feeling it all the way.

I looked down at my Big Boy in the darkness, and whispered, "He ducked you tonight, so when you get him, girl, you betta fuck him good."

A couple days later I'm in the hood chilling. Everybody was out. T-Black was posted up on Haymount Hill like this shit was sweet, So, I made sure everybody saw me and heard me say I was about to go get my dick sucked before I pulled off.

I went and switched into a rental car nobody ever saw and I changed into a woman. I paid $100 for this wig and I put on lipstick with a dress. I'm on the way back to the hood, but I'm no longer Long. You can call me Big Lauryn. On my way to the hood, I was holding a conversation, and it went like this:

"You wanna see me lil nigga? You ain't nowhere near my level. I been doing this shit!"

As I straightened my wig in the mirror at the light, I said, "I forgot to teach you how to play with appearances lil nigga."

When I got to the hood I rode right past everybody. They didn't even notice me. A different car and a wig can work wonders. As I got close to T-Black I saw there was kids around him so I circled back around. They was still there. I'm Longhead; I'm smart enough to know the timing was wrong and I can't force it. So I let it go that day.

A weekend or two after that I saw T-Black, Wayne, and Genesis in the club. You remember the boy, Genesis, Keke's baby daddy that was robbing everybody? I'll give him that, he was robbing everybody, but he didn't want no smoke from me. Well, Wayne was Genesis's cousin.

Anyway, I walked over to the pool table and put about ten *racks* on it.

I said, "You niggas out here talking about robbing me like I ain't with the shit."

Genesis said, "Long, what you talking 'bout? Ain't nobody over here gone do shit to you, homie. You the Big Homie."

I wasn't trying to hear that shit. I didn't have proof on Genesis. I only had proof on T-Black and Wayne. Genesis saw I was on some straight bullshit and they left the club. I left behind them and followed them down Bragg Boulevard. Genesis was doing 200 mph trying to get out of there.

The niggas y'all fear, fear me, my nigga. They know I don't come to play games with nobody.

The next day a motherfucker called me and said Genesis was on the Hill looking for me. I flew up there. I thought they wanted smoke. When I got there Genesis approached me.

"Man, Long, you know damn well we ain't got no problem with you," he said. I know he only came up there to see if his life was in danger. "I even told T-Black and Wayne that if they been talking about fucking with you, they know better. They know you ain't gonna play with them."

Then he made T-Black and Wayne apologize to me. I can't remember which one said it, but it fucked me up to see my lil' homie switch sides on me to be up under a nigga that people was scared of but he was scared of me. I scare the nigga you look up to.

To see T-Black in that car fucked me up.

Genesis said, "So is that shit over, Long?"

I replied, "Yeah, why not? Since you doing it like this, that shit dead."

After that, one night T-Black came home on Bunce Road to his baby mama, Antonisha's house. Somebody was waiting over there and shot him the fuck up. They only shot T-Black in the legs just to teach him a lesson, but they could have easily knocked T-Black off. I think whoever it was spared him for some odd reason.

T-Black, if you reading this, I want you to know ain't nothing soft about Longhead. You were spared with your life. You just spoke of doing something to me and could have lost your life. Thank God you got a second chance, homie. A lot of people don't get spared out here in this cold world. You never know. You reminded me of my lil' brother, Metro. That's why, my nigga, but don't ever in your life jump into a real nigga's lane again, or maybe there won't be any more chances.

T-Black is currently on State for a body. I don't see none of that shit. If you like it, I love it. The niggas

that's bodying shit know not to play with Longhead from Haymount Hill.

CHAPTER 26
Real Nigga Losses

Shit was going so crazy for me. The cops wanted me off the streets bad. It got so bad, my grandma used to warn me that if I got pulled over late night don't stop until I get around other people.

One time, me and this guy got pulled over. I was on the passenger side. I told the dude if they ran my name they coming deep. So the officer walked up, stuck his head in, and asked for license and registration. Then he walked towards the back of the car. I asked my homie what was he doing.

Next thing I knew, he had his gun in my face screaming, "Don't move motherfucker or I'll shoot!"

I held my hands up and said, "Officer, calm down. I don't got nothing."

He removed me from the car and started searching me as if he was obsessed with me, rubbing all over me saying, "Larry, Larry, Larry, O' Larry, where the guns at? Shoot anybody lately, Larry?"

I'm on the passenger side of the car. They left the driver alone. Meanwhile unmarked cars were everywhere. I thought they was gonna plant something on me.

Another time, I was on Haymount Hill late night, me and four chicks. A police came down the street and stopped in front of us.

He said, "What's up, Long?"

"Man, I ain't on shit. I'm tryna get me some pussy from these girls."

He said, "I know y'all girls feel safe out here this time of night with the killer."

One girl said, "Oh my gosh! Did y'all hear him?"

Then he told me, "I'm not gone run your name because if you had warrants you wouldn't be right here. I'm not gone search you because if you was dirty, you run like a deer; I can't catch you. I hope I'm still on the force when they make a documentary about your life."

Then he smashed the gas. Man this shit was wild!

I had so much shit going in my life. It was crazy, but I'm from Clark Street on Haymount Hill; I'm made for this shit. What else you got for me? Just send it my way, ain't nothing to it but to do it.

I remember one night I met a girl named, Reka. She was at this chick Shauny's house off of Johnson Street in Bonnie Doone. One or two of my homies was hitting Shauny, they say she had that come-back. So, when I come in the house, I spotted Reka and went crazy, straight the life of the party, crunk up fast. Now, Reka heard of me, she was from the Murk. Let me be the first to say, Reka had one of the baddest bodies I've ever seen on a young girl. I could just imagine my dick going in her. She had on some shorts that were small enough to be panties and that big butt exploded from them. Her flat stomach was smooth and soft. I wanted to fuck her right then and there. So I told Reka to come ride with me. I knew she wouldn't decline, they couldn't stop laughing at everything I said.

So she rode with me to the store. Now I'm pushing my Maserati. No disrespect to Reka, but this bitch said, "What kinda car we riding in?"

Bitch what? Do you know how many sleepless, hungry nights I had, how many times I almost threw my life away to be riding in this motherfucker right here? Bitch, bye! You better act like you know. Not only are you riding with a full-fledged gangsta, but he's ballin' too. It don't get no better than this bitch. This is a Maserati.

So, I took Reka to the store and brought her back to Shauny's house. I got shorty's number because she wasn't going with me. Bitch, I'm a boss; I get this dick sucked on every corner I turn. I don't understand, *no* when I got so many that say *yes*. What the fuck is no?

A week goes by with me talking back and forth with Reka. I talked shorty right to the rooms off Sycamore Dairy Road. I already know once I get this pussy she gone go crazy. When I say I fucked the shit out of her with this long, crooked, black dick…

Damn, hold up, let me stop the book for a second. No homo, but I'm thankful for this big dick I got, and I know how to slang that motherfucker. It done got me in some low-key spots.

So I had Reka in there saying she can't nut no more. "Long, what are you doing to me?" Reka cried out. "I get the point you're making, please stop."

I still kept going until she nutted so many times, she had to question herself, *Who the fuck is this boy?* Yeah bitch, I'm Longhead, get that shit right.

After our time in the room, Reka sat quiet the whole ride home. When I dropped her off, she text me and said that was the best, biggest dick she ever had. I smiled to myself and said I might as well add Reka to my collection because she gone.

Make a long story short, Reka moved up in my book. She is the second most loyal chick I ever met. (Dee is number one.)

Reka had breakdown moments. She had clashes with my other chicks at clubs and shit. She would say that she couldn't do this with me no more, but she always came back. Reka had a daughter named, Jordan. I fell in love with her. She used to call me her daddy. That's my dog!

I opened a business and let Reka run it. One day, we was at our house in Raeford, North Carolina, about 20 minutes from Fayetteville. I was frustrated and she could tell something was wrong, so she asked me. I told her I couldn't find a driver and I had some shit to handle.

Reka said, "I got license; I'll drive."

I said, "Fuck no, shorty, you can't drive."

Reka was so into making me happy she convinced me to let her drive. She told me she got it, she was gonna take a homegirl with her. So I let her drive. Now, to be honest, I'm a cold-hearted motherfucker, but I worried about Reka the whole time she was gone. I kept thinking, *Did I make the right decision?*

Anyway (not to go into too much detail because they might still be in the game) Reka made it safe, passed the money off, and shit got fucked up on their end. I lost a $175,000 deal. I was sick.

When she got back she asked me if she did anything wrong? I told her no.

Three days later, I lost $87,000 in a car. I was sick, homie. I was taking real nigga losses. I guess that bitch karma came back around. I know one thing, wasn't nobody taking shit from me.

I remember one day I was at home chilling. Reka came in and saw my mood.

"What's wrong?" Reka asked.

I said, "I need some money."

Do you know shorty called her baby daddy, told him something, and left the house. The next thing I know, she came back to the house with $750 dollars.

She said, "I know this ain't what you lost, but this all I could come up with."

HOLD UP! Let me stop the book. God, I wanna thank YOU for putting loyal people in my path. I guess when you real and loyal, you get blessed with real and loyal people back.

As I look back now, shorty was real as a motherfucker. Even though I wasn't broke, I just wasn't where I was. I had just took a 30-grand loss around this time.

I was fucking this pretty young girl named, Jewel. I put 3 pounds in her trunk and told her to put them up. Now this bitch go pick my lil' brother boo up late night. He trying to fuck her. They get pulled over and knocked off. Boo don't even know she got the weed in the trunk. I had to pay her lawyer fees and bond them both out of jail. A simple mistake cost me 30 grand.

Then I was fucking this Asian chick. She got pulled over and got $25,000 of my money taken. Two dudes I sent across the country came back, and got knocked off with 60 pounds of mine. I had to bond them out of jail, fly them back home, and help them with a lawyer. So Longhead was taking real nigga losses, but you know the streets don't know. We don't tell our business to the streets. Karma was being a bitch from all the people I fucked over. I was accepting what I dished out, but I'll be the first to say you'd rather see me up than down, because if I'm down, somebody got problems.

One day my lil' cousin called me and told me a white bitch named, Telisha, (the one I put Kato down with) knew all my business.

He said, "She said you been taking losses with some money. Kato telling her all your business and she telling people. I don't know cuz, but if Kato love her then he crazy 'cause we be running trains on that bitch," he added.

"Cuz, that shit ain't true," I said, playing it off.

When I hung up the phone, I said, "This tender dick nigga. I'm gonna pop him."

So I called Kato and told him to meet me at Glow House on Fleetwood. I just got the new pack in and I was about to hit him off. Now, this was my man since my early days, but this could not be tolerated.

When he walked in the door I greeted him. I went as if I was going to give him dap and hit him square in his nose. By the time he looked up, I had that Glock .40 in his face.

Now Kato *knew me* knew me, he thought it was over. My homie that was down there with me who I *fuck with* fuck with begged me not to pop him. I fuck with homie, so I respected what he said.

So I told my homie, "This nigga talk like a bitch and I'm gonna fuck him."

My homie said, "I know, Long, but don't pop him. Do that for me."

Kato stood in front of us while we held a conversation about him. He asked, "What I do, cuz?"

I told that nigga, "Shut up bitch!" Seeing him cower, I said, "You know what? I ain't gone pop you, but

I wanna see if you got a pussy between your legs. Take off your clothes, now!"

Kato stripped ass-naked. I looked him over and said, "Yeah, I see that shriveled up dick you got. What, you had that sewed down there? What, you a woman posing as a man?"

He kept asking what he did. I didn't need proof. Nobody knew what my cousin told me, but him.

So, I told him, "Leave your clothes. Let's walk outside."

So I walked him outside butt naked. When he tried to cover up his shriveled up dick, I told him to move his hands. He raced his hands out the way. I let people look at him for a little while, then I dismissed this bitch out of my presence. He rode away butt-naked and that was the end of me and Kato's friendship.

Then my lil brother, Boo, was arrested and put in the County jail for Attempted Murder, accused of shooting Mike in the eye. Have you ever seen a nigga with two eyes then see him with one? I have, and that shit scary. The damn bullet still on that boy brain. He be falling out, having seizures and shit.

Damn, so much going on. Will Longhead survive his most creative street mission yet? Only time will tell. Wait til you read what happens next…

One day somebody gonna gain the nuts to kill ole' Longhead. Until that day, he's going harder than a motherfucker.

Shout out to Reka. If you're reading this, I want you to know that $750 you gave me that time was more than what I lost because it came from your heart. In life, you don't meet too many people like you, shorty. I want you to know I cherish our friendship. In life, if you or Jordan ever need me for anything, it's done shorty. The 100% you put in didn't go unnoticed. I'm gonna put in a 150%. I love you and Jordan, always and forever.

Kato, if you reading this, you got lucky, homie. You walked away when you had a serious encounter with me, my nigga. Be thankful at night, and learn your lesson. You can't be around real niggas talking like bitches, that's what hoes do. Stop being tender dick all your life, go all out for your kids. From me to you, don't ever jump in my lane again or you might not come out so lucky.

Shout out to my connects. I'll never mention your names.

CHAPTER 27
Tell Me Y'all Joking

Damn, shit going so haywire. I'm losing so much bread, but I'm still holding shit in the road. I'm a gangsta, my nigga, not one of them dudes who say he a gangsta. I'm no gangsta because I play with that iron either. I'm a gangsta because I'm all around. I'm gonna get the money and lots of it, I'm gonna manipulate all the hoes, I'm gonna pop you if you get out of line, I'm gonna take yo' shit and dare you to act like you want a problem, I'm gonna sit in the county jail on hush, and hit all the hoes with condoms—no pillow talking—and fuck 'em with that thug passion. I'm doing all of that while moving slick, ducking the cops and rats.

That's why I say I'm a gangsta, my nigga. I know what some of y'all saying. *Who the fuck this nigga think he is? I would have stopped him.* You just a nigga with a gun, I'm a nigga with a gun and a brain. Even if you had a gun and I didn't, I can out think you with your gun. You can't hit what you can't see, and when you do see me, it's too late. Another thing that makes me a gangsta, my nigga, is that you need an army of niggas, a clique to hide behind. Not me, my nigga, I'm coming by myself. Bet that!

So, it was this nigga named Gator. Gator is from Haymount Hill, but once he got out the Feds, he went to Holiday Park off of Owen Drive with his mans named, Niko Black. Niko Black had just got out the Feds too. Him and Gator was cool before their Fed bid, so when they came home they linked up and started getting money. Lots of it too. Niko Black was from Holiday Park.

Like I told you, I don't hate on nobody getting that money, my nigga. If you asking me did they have more money than me... Fuck yeah! I'm not ashamed to admit that, my nigga. Now, if you asking me were they realer than me... Fuck no, my nigga! They knew that, or I thought they did.

So, Gator was the head dude, and then his man, Niko Black. They had a clique with some niggas named Chicken, Snoop, and Vegas. Remember those names.

One day I'm chilling on one of my regular days in the hood on Haymount Hill. I got a phone call. A motherfucker told me that Kato broke into Niko Black's house and hit him for $30,000 and some clothes. Niko was telling everybody that it was just alcohol money.

I said, "Damn, I wish I would have got that free thirty if he felt like that. I'm taking losses over here too!"

I got off the phone with homie. Even though I'm not fucking with Kato no more, I still try to wrap my mind on what and how was Kato linked in to find out where Niko Black lived. I couldn't put a connection together in my mind, so I figured he just got lucky and might of ran across his house. Hell, even a trash can get lucky and get a steak every now and then.

After that, I let it go. I wasn't thinking about the next man's money or losses. I was taking my own losses, just not like that though. Ain't nobody taking shit over here.

So, a few days passed, and I get a call from D'so. D'so is my homie Meat-Meat's big brother. I can sense urgency in his voice. He tells me to meet him on the Hill in thirty minutes.

When I got up there, I wasn't ready for what I heard.

D'so told me, "Man, Long, I just left Gator and Niko Black's detail shop off of Owen Drive. They call me inside and locked the door and told me sit down. Then Gator said they know Kato broke into Niko Black's house. They rewinded the camera back and somebody ID'd him." Then D'so dropped a bomb on me. "Then this motherfucker said, what's up with Long? Is he really 'bout that shit like they say his is, because my lawyer told me the only thing he can't beat is a gun charge if you get caught with it. But murder charges and all of that, he eat them up."

So he said by the time Gator finished talking, Chicken jumped up and said, "Let's kidnap that bitch ass nigga!"

Then Gator said, "So what's up with that nigga, Long?"

D'so said he told them, "Man, y'all called me over here for this? Y'all know damn well if you go up there fucking with that boy, a motherfucker gone get fucked up. Now, y'all know just like I know, that boy ain't meant to be played with. Go up there and fuck with him and find out for yourself. Let me outta here."

So I said, "What now?"

This my homie, Meat-Meat's big brother so he knew me good, and I know he wouldn't play with me about no shit like this. Still I was confused. Did they know what they getting themselves into? And why did they say Kato broke into Niko Black's house, but screaming my name? Then you talking about murder charges without putting a name on it? Reader, has this motherfucker lost his mind? He barking up the right tree, that's for damn sure. This right up my alley.

So, I got Gator's number and called him aggressively. He picked up on the first ring.

I told him, "Man, this Long, you need to come out and meet me now."

"It's too late now, fam. I'll meet you at the mall tomorrow. I been meaning to holla at you anyway," he claimed.

So we agreed to meet at the mall.

The next day I met him at the mall dolo. I went by myself to let him know, in so many words, I'll fuck you and your whole clique up by myself homie, with no clique. When I approached him, he got two niggas with him, standing with enough distance so he could talk. They looked like they might have had them straps on them, but I don't see that shit.

I'm sitting across the table with probably the biggest nigga in the city at this time.

I spoke, "What seems to be the problem?"

He said, "Long, man, I don't got no problem with you. It's just that Kato broke into my man Niko Black house and we got him on camera doing it."

"What the fuck that got to do with me though?"

"Now I know Kato from up yo' way and them boys can't move on something like that without your say-so or you knowing. But then I heard you just stripped Kato butt-naked, so I'm confused."

I told that nigga, "You've been misguided, homie. Dudes do what they wanna do. I don't have no kids; I don't own them niggas over there. And far as Kato breaking into yo man crib, I don't know shit about that. Plus, that's none of my business."

"Long, I respect that. Maybe it was a misunderstanding."

So, as the conversation dying down, we was about to end it, but I could tell this nigga wanted a war—which I'm down for. So, before he got ready to leave, this nigga said some shit that let me know he wanted a war.

"Long, how will you feel if we did something bad to Kato?"

Because really he just tried me on some sucker shit, I looked that nigga in his eyes and spoke these words,

"I don't give a fuck what y'all do to Kato; I don't fuck with him. That's between y'all and Kato. But if it was somebody I fuck with, then you gone have a problem on your hand."

He said he respect what I said.

I asked him, "What if something was to happen to your man, Niko Black?"

He quickly got defensive. "Nah, Niko Black chilling. He ain't got nothing to do with this," he claimed.

"It was his house that got broke in, right?" I said.

"Yeah, but he chilling, homie. Everything cool."

I guess this nigga loved Niko Black. He didn't want nothing to happen to his man.

Make a long story short, at the end of the convo, I told that nigga I'm fucked up out here.

"I need you to throw a dog a bone. Straight up!" I said.

He said, "Long, what you need?"

I said, "Shit I need 10 racks."

"Oh, that's no problem. I'll get that to you tomorrow." And we departed.

The next day, a nigga dropped me off ten grand, cash. I counted every dollar. It better had not been a dollar short. I'm motherfucking Longhead; I will breathe out fire and spit blood before anybody play with me in these streets. He knew his best option was to come off that money. Fuck the wolves, I am *the* Wolf that lead the pack. He came over here fucking with me, I wasn't even on their line when I should have went over there and took all that shit.

Shit got real a few weeks later. I was in Bob's barber shop sitting in the chair when Vegas walked in and said he needed to holla at me. Immediately, I got on the defensive.

"Long, it ain't nothing like that," Vegas said. "I'll holla at you when you finish."

When I'm done getting my hair cut, he walked out with me. I let him hop in that big-boy four-door truck, a big-boy rental.

This nigga said, "Look Long, them niggas Gator and Niko Black is crazy if they think I'ma go after you. I'm not 'bout to lose my life fucking with you. I know better! But them niggas got a $50,000 hit on your head right now."

I got so mad when he said that, I told him to get the fuck out my car.

He then pleaded his case, "Long, man, I'll call them and put them on speaker right now. I ain't on no bullshit. I just know better than to take that bread. If it was anybody else, I would have done it, but on my mama, they crazy as hell if I try you. How am I gonna enjoy the money? What I'ma do, leave it to my kids?"

"Man, I ain't tryna hear all that shit. Call them."

So, he called them. While the phone was ringing he begged me not to say nothing. Little did he know, I was anxious to hear them attempt to talk about killing me.

A familiar voice answered the phone. Then Vegas whispered, "I got that bitch-ass nigga Long right here in front of me. What y'all want me to do? Is that money right?"

They spoke fast, "Hell yeah, that money right. Handle that bitch-ass nigga."

Now readers, I can't tell you my feelings right then when I'm listening to niggas plotting to kill ole' Longhead. I do know one thing, if they wanted a problem or not they had one on their hand now.

So I pulled off with Vegas in the car. Instantly he said, "Long, where you going. I'm on your side."

I told him, "Chill out, you get a pass for right now. Ride with me real quick."

I pulled up on Haymount Hill. This nigga was scared shitless. He thought I was gonna do him in. I pulled up at Mrs. Judy house, Tab's mama.

I said, "You know, since they want me dead and they willing to pay, this what we gone do... I want you to go get somebody from over there for a witness, drive over here, and chase me around the house, then shoot in the air. Get the money and come split it with me after they pay you."

When I finished telling him the plan, that nigga sat on the passenger side with his mouth open.

"Man, you came up with all that, that fast? Boy they not lying when they say you a smart motherfucker. Aye Long, I'm scared of you, boy. You dangerous! Them niggas done fucked up."

I dropped him back off at the barber shop, then stashed the car behind Tab's mama house. I sat on the porch. When Vegas pulled up, the kid Snoop from Holiday Park was driving. Vegas jumped out and I ran, but when Vegas got around the house, I had two niggas back there with the choppers.

He jumped back, thought I had double-crossed him.

I told him, "Man, they here for me. Shoot the gun in the air and get out of here."

He squeezed about five shots in the air. As I looked in the sky, I thought, *damn, them bullets was meant for me.*

Vegas ran, jumped back in the car, and skidded off. Me and them two niggas jumped in the truck and pulled off.

See, if you can't think, don't ever cross paths with me. You have not a winning chance.

So, on the way out the hood, I called my grandmother. When she picked up I told her that if anybody called and said I was shot, it's a lie. I'm okay. I'm on the way to my girlfriend's house, so don't worry about me.

She said, "Well, why would somebody say you got shot?"

"Grandma, you know how they lie on me."

"Well okay, I'm glad you called me. I would have been worried about you."

See, I'm considerate. I know this woman love me, so I couldn't trick her. I had to make sure she knew what's up.

I got dropped off at this bad bitch house named, Astrid. Astrid was off the record, and she was fine as shit.

Before I got out the car, I told them two niggas they had to pass the word on because I was not going to say I got shot out my own mouth. I'm not gonna lie on myself when I know it ain't true. They agreed then went to pass on the message while I sat in the house with Astrid.

This my word, about an hour later Astrid's phone rang. I was sitting right beside her watching TV. When she picked up I could hear a girl screaming, "Oh my God, girl! Where you at? Long just been shot! Girl, they say he in ICU!"

I could see the confused look on Astrid's face when she looked at me sitting beside her. I signaled for her to be quiet and get off the phone. When she ended the call, she said,

"Long, what the fuck is going on? Why is people saying you shot?"

I spat back, "Do I look shot? Fuck no! Girl, you know how people lie on me. Just don't tell them different, let them think and say what they want."

Before long, they had it on Facebook saying I was dead. One post said, pray for me because I was in critical condition. People was on there commenting... The shit was wild! I knew I was known, but damn.

My homie that dropped me off came back to pick me up. We met Vegas in a small town called, Spring Lake. It was night time so I was low-key.

When I hopped in the car, my homie said, "Man, what the fuck do you know about what's going on? KooKoo and yo' family was at the hospital trying to find you, and the police was there with them asking where you at, and who shot you? Their life could be in danger."

I was tripping.

He said, "Bruh, the whole city trying to figure out if you dead or what. People been blowing our phone lines up asking what hospital you at. This shit done got out of hand. Man, everybody looking for you! My mama trying to find out if you okay..."

I sat in the backseat on the way to meet Vegas. Finally, I spoke,

"Them niggas tried to kill me, bruh. Tell me they joking, right? They somewhere loving this."

I'm motherfucking Longhead from Haymount Hill, Clark Street. The people you sending to hit me, respect me. Have you lost your mind? I'm a legend around this motherfucker, homie. Before these niggas take your money to hit me, they will tell you, fuck you and your money; find him your fucking self!

I went and met Vegas. They gave him a portion of the money. He split it down the middle with me.

Then Vegas said, "Man, everywhere I go, they talking 'bout you shot. I heard some people say you were dead. Man, you fooled everybody, Long. What you gone do to them niggas?"

I said, "Man, them niggas want me dead, so I gave them a painted picture of what it sounds like. Get the rest of that money from them."

"That's my word, I'ma get it, Long. What about them lil' niggas that look up to you and don't know you didn't get shot. What if they kill me?"

I said, "Well Vegas, I didn't plan that far for you. Your name is attached to shooting one of the realest niggas from this city. If I was you, homie, I'll lay low for a little while. Shit can get real out here."

Before we departed, he told me he was going to lay low. I went back to Astrid's house.

I came out about a week later and decided to go to the Hill with my same homie driving. Now when I got out the car, I started moving slow, holding my hip. Mind you, I ain't ever said I got shot, but they too blind to see that far. All the girls bumrushed me, asking if I was ok, and where did I get shot at (nosey bitches.)

In the weakest voice I could muster, I said, "Back up please, I don't feel like talking."

I waved my homie over and he backed them up for me. "Bruh don't feel like talking," he told them.

I moved around super slow, still holding my hip. Finally, I told my homie I was ready to go.

See, when it comes to this game you gotta cover your tracks and play it all the way through.

Back in the truck, my homie didn't even know I was about to do what I was just doing. I play the game as it comes.

He said, "Man, where do you come up with this shit? You deserve an Oscar."

I told him, "Naw, when it comes to this game, I'm a playing motherfucker."

Later, this is the story I got. Somebody waited outside Niko Black's new house and hit him 17 times. They say the shooter jumped out of a trash can. He survived. I guess his God wasn't ready for him, although he remained in the hospital for a long time. I heard he had $60,000 in the middle console of the car when the police came to the scene. I even heard one of his homies visited him at the hospital and Niko Black assured him that the shooter wasn't coming for his money, they came for his soul.

Then, I heard somebody caught Gator in broad daylight and dumped all into his car in the middle of traffic. Now with his man almost losing his life, and somebody tryna kill him, Gator couldn't take it anymore. He packed he and his family up and left Fayetteville, with his man Niko Black on a hospital bed and Chicken scrambling.

One night, somebody waited outside Chicken's chick house and hit Chicken's homie the fuck up in a case of mistaken identity. Chicken pulled up five minutes later! I say Chicken was lucky.

Another time, I heard somebody caught Chicken in traffic and chased him. They hit him, but he got away.

I got Chicken's number and called him. He said, "Man, Long, you won. Gator moved outta town, Niko Black fucked all the way up, they left me for dead. You a smart motherfucker. How did you track everybody down the way you did?"

I told that nigga, "I don't know what you talking about, but don't ever let me catch you in these streets talking about doing something to Long." I made him apologize, and after he did it, I still told him to be careful and don't get caught slipping.

He said, "Damn, Long, you win. Everywhere I turn, a motherfucker shooting at me, man."

I hung up the phone on him.

This shit was too wild! The only people who knew I didn't get shot was my grandma, Astrid, Vegas, and my two homies. I tricked my whole city, police and all. You know what they say, if you can trick them, you can beat them. I guess I can beat my whole city. You think you really got what it takes to fuck with Longhead? Fuck no! Get your thinking skills up.

Well, I guess now everybody gone know I didn't get shot with this book I'm putting out.

The old get-money click was broken up. D'so told them clowns something they already knew, but some people just have to see it for themselves.

While all this going on, a dude named Jamie from Red Springs got abducted. Somebody held him somewhere then went to his stash house and hit him for a $150,000 worth of money and work. They put that on me too. At the same time, this girl was running round telling people I killed her brother... All kinds of crazy shit.

Man, I know Longhead time got to be about up. They got to be on his line downtown. I know he on fire with the cops. They blame too much on him. He can feel it, but one thing for sure, he makes his bed so he's willing to lay in it. Watch what happens next in Long's life.

Gator, if you reading this, I hope you learn your lesson by fucking with Longhead. You can't throw your weight around with money when you dealing with a nigga as smart as me, with my kind of heart and nuts. If I ever think you having a thought about jumping in my lane, you won't get so lucky. D'so tried to warn you. I guess you had to see for yourself.

Niko Black, if you reading this, my advice to you is you let $30,000 you lost in a break-in run you up on a snag. This the game! Y'all was getting plenty money and you got side tracked. How them slugs feel when they entering your body? I hear them shits be hot. Naw, I asked you because I ain't never been shot, so I figure you could tell me, sucker. Don't ever play with me. I'm

the real deal, as you can see. Jump in my lane again. I dare you to.

Gator and Niko Black are currently locked up on a Heroin Conspiracy Charge.

Vegas, if you reading this, stay yo' slick ass away from me or you might not slither away next time.

Chicken, if you reading this, you weak, homie. You apologized to me but you was just saying 'Let's kidnap that bitch ass nigga.' Bet you don't feel that way now. You pissy scared of me.

Snoop, the driver, was murdered. May God bless his soul. LMAO.

CHAPTER 28
Hard Headed

I knew it was a cell with my name on it. I knew it, I just couldn't put my finger on it. I know I had made my bed and one day I had to lay in it. To really be honest, I thought I wouldn't ever go to prison. I thought I moved too slick to go to prison. When I used to bail my homies out of jail for dumb shit all the time, I used to ask them, "Damn, do you like it out here or in there?" They would run back and forth to the county jail. Me? I avoided frivolous encounters with a cell.

I knew it was coming. Everybody wanted to see me fall. Every police officer in the city, hoes I had manipulated and fucked over that thought I was their man. All the niggas I had put in their place and couldn't do nothing about it. Everybody wanted me far out the way. Hell, I know dudes I had right up under me who wanted me out the way.

So, I knew it was coming one day. The eyes of man are never satisfied. How could I ever make these motherfuckers happy? I was a gangsta. A good nigga. I punished and took from those that deserved it, and gave to those in need. I was a good nigga out there for real, for real. How can you not fuck with real niggas if you in the game? How can you ever go against real niggas, my nigga? Learn how to live and let live.

My road was coming to an end fast. Tab called me one day. I was in my spot sitting around 100 years.

"Brother, where you at?" Tab asked. "It's a thousand police on this back street."

I grabbed what I could, and my homies grabbed the rest. As soon as we got a couple houses down on feet, we watched them hit the very same house we just left out of. Man, if Tab wouldn't have called me I would have been fucked up, homie. God watches over me.

Then, they hit my house with the inground pool. I had fucked this young, pretty girl named Zykia that night. She woke me up early in the morning at about 6:30 and told me she had to go get her son because her grandma had to be to work. I took her. By the time I made it back to the house, it was flooded with *unmarks.* I rode right past them. They didn't even notice me.

I was later pulled over in a traffic stop. The only reason I didn't run was because they claimed they were looking for somebody else. They knew I would have ran. In the traffic stop, when he told me I had a warrant, I thought I didn't show up for a ticket. Once he put me in the backseat, he showed me his computer. It said, *we have Larry Everett*. Then, he told me I had a federal warrant out of Arkansas, so he took me downtown.

He told me he had somebody who wanted to meet me. I knew whoever this was wanted to get some shit off their chest. He put me in this room and said the person would be with me in a second.

I knew they were watching me so I put my head down. Five minutes later, the door popped open and in walked an officer I never saw since I've been in the streets.

He spoke, "Long, how you doing? Do you know who I am?"

"Naw, I don't, but what you want with me? I ain't did shit," I replied.

Then he got aggressive. "Don't give me that bullshit! You've been a pain in every department in this city's ass. We are tired of your shit! You think you gone get away now? We got you, but I have to tell you, you one of the smartest guys we ever investigated. It took me and 58 other agents to get you in that seat you sitting in."

He looked at me for a response. I said, "Damn, you didn't need all those people for little ole' me."

"Bullshit! Don't give me that. You kill anybody lately?" He asked me about some murders.

I said, "Sir, I'm ready to go now. You're scaring me. I need a lawyer."

"We already know your tough ass ain't gone talk to us."

Then he showed me a picture of a guy and told me, "He better not come up dead, or we gonna get your ass!"

I said, "Oh my gosh, you're scaring me, sir. Can you take me to my cell."

To make a long story short, Lil' Earl, one of my lil' homies served a police they sent at him. Then, they tapped his phone. They waited on me to call. When I called him, they could tap my phone. I changed my number so much they couldn't keep tabs on me, so they went and got warrants to tap my phone the next time I called. Then they tapped everybody phone I called, so it didn't matter how much I changed my number.

Am I mad at Lil' Earl? He didn't know, but I am pissed at the lil' nigga for not changing his number though. I always used to tell them to change their numbers and he didn't listen. All he had to do was change his number one time and he would have lost them. They even had me on recordings telling him to change his number. I didn't even know he was bugged. Just my instincts.

So, that's why I'm mad at lil' Earl. He didn't listen and caused me to miss the birth of my daughter, along with my freedom. That's why I teach people around me, so they don't crash and crash me with them. He still didn't listen though. I bet you he knows it's real now. Listen to the fucking Big Homie! You think he speaking for nothing, or changing his number every week for nothing?

The Feds flew me to Memphis, dropped me off, and drove me to the CCA in Mason, Tennessee. Then they drove me to Little Rock, Arkansas, Pulaski County Jail. (You can smoke in their county jail.)

Here I was in a state I'd never been in, down here holding shit down with all the gang bangers, still dolo, my nigga. That's how I rock. I didn't talk about my case with nobody. They knew I was a real nigga. They called me Carolina.

In October of 2013, me, my driver, and my cousin, Felicia was charged in a drug conspiracy.

I knew time was winding down.

Lil Earl, if you reading this, I want you to know, homie, I move too smooth to be in prison. You fucked up by not changing your number like I told you time and time again. Being hard-headed cost me my freedom. A simple mistake can cost niggas their lives. This should be a life lesson for you and all them lil' niggas out there. You moved wrong and cost me the throne. You better be glad I got love for you, lil' homie,

or I would have taken this personal. I know you downtown on a First-degree murder charge, I'm still gonna say a prayer for you at night, homie. I'm a real nigga, my nigga, the real deal.

Tab, if you reading this, I want you to know I love you sister, you and Mrs. Judy. Tab, we grew up together, and even though you're a female, we had similar struggles growing up. I love you, shorty. Haymount Hill, we in this motherfucker! I love you too, Mrs. Judy. Breakfast on me, Mrs. Judy.

Fayetteville drug trafficking ring spurred first use of wiretaps

By [illegible] Staff writer
Posted Apr 22, 2015 at [illegible]
Updated Apr 22, 2015 at [illegible]

Testimony Wednesday in a case involving two men accused of drug trafficking illustrates the elaborate way Fayetteville police used wiretaps for the first time.

The wiretaps and GPS monitoring devices helped police track a package in which more than a pound of cocaine was inserted into two stuffed animals and shipped from Arizona to Fayetteville in July 2012, according to the testimony in Cumberland County Superior Court.

The electronic surveillance led to the indictments of at least four people, including Fayetteville residents [illegible] and [illegible], whose trial on charges of conspiring to traffic cocaine continues today. Both men have extensive prison records and could face more than 15 years in prison if convicted.

Fayetteville police narcotics Detective Joseph Delpizzo testified that the case began with a traffic stop in Hammond in October 2010. The stop resulted in the arrest of a man on drug charges, Delpizzo testified that police seized the man's cell phone, which provided contact information for a drug ring. Using those contacts, he said, a police criminal informant then made 16 purchases of marijuana and cocaine from the ring, setting the stage for the wiretaps and tracking devices by late 2011.

Police filed an affidavit requesting the wiretaps with the State Bureau of Investigation, the only law enforcement agency in the state that can legally use them, said [illegible] Jarman, the SBI's assistant special agent in charge of the Fayetteville region.

Jarman said he sent the request to the state attorney general, whose approval is also required. From there, it went to the chief judge of the state Supreme Court, who selected a three-judge panel that gave final approval in February 2012 to use the wiretaps for 30 days, Jarman said.

The affidavit would have to be submitted nine more times because of the expiration date and requests for wiretaps on additional phones as the case progressed, Jarman testified.

Delpizzo said police wanted to use the wiretaps "to bring Fayetteville into the 21st century" in an effort to stop drug trafficking and other crimes. He described the drug ring police were after as among the bigger ones in Fayetteville at the time.

Delpizzo said the commercial phone carrier relayed the taped phone conversations and text messages to the SBI in Raleigh, which sent them to Fayetteville police.

By then, Delpizzo said, police had identified a home off [illegible] Road where the drug ring operated. He said police rented a nearby apartment and were able to use high-tech cameras to watch members of the ring talking on the phone.

Using the wiretaps, police learned that a member of the drug ring was heading to Tucson, Arizona, where he would pay for the cocaine using money collected from "investors," Delpizzo said. The cocaine was then mailed back to Fayetteville in a white box through the U.S. Postal Service. The cocaine was placed inside two stuffed horses, which were wrapped in a gift bag and surrounded by tubs of Play-Doh and Hot Wheels cars.

Delpizzo said police intercepted a text message that provided a tracking number for the package, and he said a postal inspector retrieved the box at the Post Office on Green Street on July 4, 2012.

In his testimony, Delpizzo didn't say who else in the drug ring was indicted along with [illegible] and [illegible]. But he identified the ring's leader as Larry Donnell Everett and the middleman in Arizona as Everett's cousin, Felicia Camelia Diggs.

Diggs and Everett were under federal indictment on cocaine-related charges in Arkansas in November 2013, when Diggs was shot to death in her front yard on Paddlefish Drive in Cumberland County.

According to published reports at the time, Diggs' lawyer, Mark Jesse, said Diggs had complained about feeling threatened because of the federal case. He said she knew details about drug trafficking between Arizona and Arkansas and may have been killed because she provided information.

In the Fayetteville case, Delpizzo called Diggs the middleman between Everett's ring and people he described as "Mexican nationals."

Everett, Diggs and another Fayetteville man, identified by police as Deldrick D. Sanders, were indicted federally after Sanders was pulled over for speeding on Aug. 3, 2012, on Interstate 40 in Russellville, Arkansas. Published reports say lawmen found 2 pounds of cocaine in his trunk.

No one has been charged with Diggs' murder.

CHAPTER 29
Why Blame Me?

As I sat in Pulaski County Jail in Little Rock, Arkansas, I called home and this bitch said,

"Can you take bad news while you in there?"

"Yeah why, what's up?"

"Somebody murdered your cousin Felicia last night," she informed me.

It fucked me up. Then, it fucked me up when I was on the news and in the newspaper, not only in Fayetteville, North Carolina, but Arkansas as well. When I looked up and saw myself on the news down there, I already knew what they was planning. They did just what I thought too.

The police in Fayetteville and the Feds said I had my cousin, Felicia, murdered. Somebody waited outside her house and shot her dead in her front yard. It tore me apart. She was a woman with three kids. She is the daughter of my grandmother, Mrs. May's daughter, my Aunt Dot's child. You think I would make my grandmother and aunt cry?

My family split up. Some believed I had something to do with it because of the police theory, and some don't believe it at all.

I had a dream while in Little Rock's jail. In the dream, my cousin came to me and said, "*Why everybody saying you killed me*?"

I told her, "Cuz, I promise you I had nothing to do with that. I love you."

Then she disappeared. I haven't seen her since. Her murder is still unsolved to this day. I have an idea of who killed her, but you know we keep it in the streets around here. If I have the slightest idea you touched one of mine, that beast in Longhead will be awakened again.

Two months before I went to court, I had another dream. Somebody in a hoody placed a newborn baby on my bed. In the dream, I grabbed the baby and hugged the baby tight. Then when I tried to look in the baby's face, it had strength of a grown person and snatched back before I could see its face. The baby put his mouth to my left ear and spoke these words,

"*God said HE got you!*"

Then the baby disappeared. If I'm lying, I'm flying. I kept it real with you this whole book, and just told it how it happened.

When I went to court, the officer in that room from Fayetteville flew down there. He tried to get the judge to break me off. I was only on a 5 to 40 guideline bracket. I had no record, and no felonies. If you know anything about the Feds, they give you your time based off your record. I was supposed to get only 5 years, but the judge gave me leadership role, and hit me with an enhancement of 2 extra years.

I was sentenced to 87 months in federal prison.

What you just read, ladies and gentlemen, is the legacy and life of Longhead the Gangsta. Thank you for reading and purchasing my book. Thank you!

Shout out to the Small family. If you reading this, I want y'all to know I'm a cold motherfucker, true indeed, but I would have never hurt y'all like that. Even though most of y'all shitted on me when I was a kid, I would have never hurt y'all, especially not my grandmother. For the ones that still feel I did, I can't change y'all minds. For the ones that don't feel this way, thanks for knowing better. I love y'all. Family is all we got. I know it's gonna be strange on holidays now, so I'm not even gonna come around and destroy your holidays. Y'all have fun. One Love to the Small family. R.I.P. James Small, the founder.

R.I.P. Felicia, aka Krada. I want you to know if you can hear me, cuz, I love you! I told you in that dream when you asked me that I didn't have nothing to do with that. Place any burden on me, but please not that LORD. I love you, cuz, until we meet again. Your kids can come to me for anything. I just hope they don't hate me too. Family forever cuz.

R.I.P. Cuz

CHAPTER 30
My Change

Me, Longhead, I see life different now. The old dog took enough of a beating, mentally. Like Juvenile said, *I rather see it on TV than to see it in person.* I have a daughter now. Her name is Lauryn. Young Jeezy said, one day you'll have kids, and how you gone explain all the shit you did? When I hear this little girl call me dad, it's a feeling I can't even explain. Pure Innocence.

Some shit I've done was dumb, and I wish I could take it back, but I can't. Some shit was justified under the Street Law. I've had time to reflect on my life, I wanna see my grandkids grow up one day. Yep ole' Longhead wanna be a granddaddy.

My jersey should be hung up in the middle of the city of Fayetteville, North Carolina for the way I put on for my city. I retire, homie. I submitted my retirement papers, I'm out. When you see me, let me be. Don't ever in your life think I forgot how to put it down though, homie. I'm with the shit. I'm just giving it all up for that little girl, and my grandmother. Did prison stop a nigga like me? Fuck no! Did somebody scare me out? Picture that. I just want out. I played the game at a hell of a level. I gave you motherfuckers an unforgettable show. In the immortal words of Tyrese, *what more do you want from me???*

I took my lick like a man. I ain't ever been shot. (Kind of remind me of that Jay Z song when he said, *I remain without a stain on my shirt.*) Ain't nobody ever robbed me, and when the Feds stepped in, I went *right* instead of *left*. I kept it "G" like I am.

For those of you who don't know about the Feds, it's something called an FOIA, short for the Freedom of Information Act. You can go on there and look at anybody case in the Feds and see how they handled their business, see if they went right instead of left. Now, the Feds ain't gone say, *he snitched.* It's gonna say he received a *5K1*.

A 5K1 means you assisted the government with something you know. There is also something called a Rule 35. A Rule 35 means you been going back and forth to testify on niggas after you got your time. Yeah, expose these suckers.

I'm looking to invest in stocks and bonds these days. Before I go out to clubs, I'd rather hang out with my daughter and do comedy shows. There's nothing I haven't done out there, homie. So, ketchup, mustard.

This is my message to you: go hard or go home. I put in work from the time I was 13 years old until the Feds got me. I went hard as a motherfucker too, kinda like a movie. I'm out now, just don't jump in my lane.

What more can I say, except for what Mo been telling y'all this whole time. Mo knew something we would all found out later and it went like this:

"Aye Longhead, when it comes to this game, you a playing motherfucker!

THE END

EPILOGUE

"Destiny baby, why are you crying?"

"I don't know... I feel sorry for you. You've been through a lot, and I bet you that wasn't all of it. It's more, ain't it, Richard?" Destiny said, between sniffles.

"Yes baby, there's more. I couldn't tell it all in one story, but I covered some good pointers. Destiny, baby, what's that look in your eyes? I've seen that look too many times."

Destiny stopped crying and flipped out. "You a fucking liar, Richard! Richard's not even your fucking name. Long, Richard... whoever da fuck you are, it's not fair. All you do is manipulate girls and hurt people!" Destiny screamed.

"Destiny, baby, I love you. Calm down, baby. I know I didn't give you my name they gave me at birth. I don't like that name, I was gonna change it to Richard, so I was testing it out to see how I like being called Richard. I still gave you my heart; it's only one of those, and it's real. So, come here pretty girl, don't run your blood pressure up. No worries, I'ma protect you."

"Okay, Richard," she said in a different tone as if she was bipolar. "I hear you, but you have to do me a favor, Richard."

"Yes, Destiny, anything for you."

"Don't call me Destiny no more. Call me, Dora."

"What baby?"

"You heard me," Destiny said. "And the two things Mo taught you... you were wrong about one thing."

"What's that, Dora?" I said confused. *Who was she? What have I turned her into?*

"When it comes to this game, Richard, you are a playing motherfucker."

"So what was I wrong about, Destiny. I—I meant, Dora?"

"We not graveyard friends. Mo didn't teach you that. We graveyard niggas, my nigga. That's what Mo taught you, and that's what we are."

TO BE CONTINUED...

EXCLUSIVE INTERVIEW WITH LONG

Reporter: I mean gosh, I read your book. Your life is astonishing! Wouldn't you say?

Long: (LOL) I mean, if you say so. I just live it.

Reporter: I assume with the exposure this book will get, they can see what it's like, right?

Long: I mean, people take things for what they want to. If two people read a story, they'll come up with two different o outlooks on it.

Reporter: Let's get more personal, Long. I see you mention your daughter, but you never mention her mother. Why?

Long: (LMAO) Who is that?

Reporter: I mean, you do have a daughter, right?

Long: Yes.

Reporter: (LMAO) You a wild nigga! Ok, let's move on. What's next?

Long: I'm thinking of a documentary, 4m Da Corner 2 Da Castle. It just depends, also No More Game for Free. Basically, just hustling from nothing, you know.

Reporter: Oh ok, that's what's up. I'll be on the lookout for that. Do you have a woman? If so, does she know your real name?

Long: (LMAO) Aye, where y'all get the reporter from? He's a wild nigga. Yes, actually I do got a woman. All I'ma say is she special. I fucks with her the long way. And yes, she knows me.

Reporter: Who is she?

Long: Well in due time, you'll know. But to be honest, I'll tell you this. When we first linked up, she was scared of me. She heard so many horrendous stories about me. She now says I'm nothing like what she's heard. I'm super nice! Shout out to her daughter too. That's my dog.

Reporter: So, are you out the game for real for real?

Long: It's like this: I'm out, but please don't jump in my lane. That's why they got white lines in the road, so you can stay in yo' lane. The streets ain't made for everybody, that's why they got sidewalks.

Reporter: Before I go, I know you love your grandmother. Your bond is like no other.

Long: Oh my! That's my heart, no question.

Reporter: Any more shoutouts you wanna give before we wrap it up?

Long: Shout out to my, pops. You a real nigga. Even though you left me for dead, you came back and made it right. I respect it. Shout out to KooKoo. I know our bond ain't strong, but you still pushed me out. I'm glad y'all left me anyway. That brought the best out of me. Shout out to my sisters, Kiera, Mek-Mek, Chug, Eliza, Drika, and Khapresha. Shout out to my lil brother, Boo. He went to trial and beat the Attempted Murder on Mike. Now he downtown on a body he didn't commit. Hold on, lil' bro, freedom coming. Shout out to Jig, my motherfucking nigga. Shout out to Lauryn. Daddy loves you. When you get older, you'll understand. Shout out to my mentors that gave me the game growing up. Mo, Kojack, and D-Ray. And all the real niggas I met along the way, I'm motherfucking Longhead from Haymout Hill, Clark Street. If you ever see me in public, don't think I forgot how to put certain shit down. I'm 'bout this motherfucker 4'm Da Corner 2 Da Castle. They making books off the shit I did!

SNEAK PEEK

Do You Know the Person Beside You

When you around dudes, most of you say y'all are niggas from the heart, that y'all ready to go all out for each other. You never realize you don't have shit in common. That's why y'all fall out over frivolous shit. You never identified any differences you have between you. Just because you from the same hood, you say y'all homies. Get the fuck outta here!

Dudes build foundations on the weakest shit ever. You wonder why he turned on you? You wonder why he set you up? You wonder why he crossed you and fucked your wife? You wonder why he took the stand on you? Huh?

What the fuck was you thinking? You let a nigga in your circle just because you come from the same area? That's the dumbest shit I ever heard of in life! Are you dudes stupid or you just dumb as fuck? Do you love your life? If you don't love you, how can you love me? An old man told me one time: If I'm loving you, and you loving you, then who the fuck is loving me?

When a nigga come around you, in your head you're supposed to say, "There goes my nigga, twenty."

Because that motherfucker will get you 20 years in prison and go about his life like he ain't did no wrong.

Do You Know the Person Beside You helps you figure dudes out. I been reading these dudes with some hell of ways to do it.

I can't give you this shit for free, that's why it's called, *Do You Know the Person Beside You.* You got to pay for this shit. I almost lost my life numerous of nights to obtain this knowledge. I tell you this, you don't get this overnight. Hell, some people go through shit and still don't get this. You have to seek knowledge and have understanding. I wanted this shit. When I do anything, I'm not trying to fail. Fuck that. Once it's over, your story is no good. Feel me?

All the men that's fighting their appeals and finding the loop holes, I salute you, my nigga. Keep your head up. Better days are coming. I'm writing this in prison myself.

Anyway, back to what you purchased, if you follow these rules you will not lose. If you do, call me because you've done something wrong. If a dude or a girl was to come in my life, or even if they already in my life, they not gonna come out and say, "Long, I'm a thief."

I need to know this though. I need to know who's around me at all times. So, it's up to me to find out who they are since they ain't telling me. So when I go pick them up in my car, I have $3,500 dollars in $100 bills on the passenger seat folded up where they can see it. (It's something about them C-notes a motherfucker can't resist.) I will pull up at the store, get out, and give them time to steal it.

Now here's a catch. If they steal it, you can't say nothing. You can't expose your hand, So if you don't got it to lose, don't put it down there. Just know when you drop them off that night they some petty stealing motherfuckers. You can X them off your friend list.

This shit here for players, my nigga. If you ain't one, this book ain't for you. You don't want them to know your motives. That's another reason you don't say nothing. I'd rather a person cost me $3500, than cost me my life down the road. Feel me? If it took $500 dollars for you to come out the closet and identify yourself to me, that's a win-win. Now, if they give that money back, look and see if it's been unfolded. That means they thought about it, but figured it wasn't enough. If it's still folded, that means they just passed one of many test I will put on their ass.

Sometimes, or most of the times, temptation will bring a person to the light of who they really are. No more game teach you all kind of ways to do this. In order to be around me, you will be tested without knowing.

It's only a test. If you are who say you are, then you have no worries, but if you're not, I will find out who's the person beside me. Life is too valuable. You only get one, you won't help in destroying mine. Bitch or nigga, it doesn't matter. If you around me, I will test you.

Don't get it twisted. If a man that won't steal $500 dollars, that doesn't mean he won't steal $50,000. When the price goes up, the mind frame changes. Now, he can think of more shit to do. His mind is opened up with different avenues to take. But no worries, I'll show you how to spot them too. You gotta follow the steps though.

If you're reading this, that means you read *4M Da Corner 2 Da Castle*. You're gonna love, *Do You Know the Person Beside You.* Check it out coming in a book store near you soon.

Long, from Haymount Hill, Clark Street in this motherfucker. Real niggas, I salute. I've been put in some dark moments in life and I'm gonna teach you everything I've learned and what my mentors taught me.

A man is not made overnight, he is made by his challenges and controversies. This is who I became, so this is who I am.